TEST ITEMS FOR HECHT'S

Physics:

ALGEBRA/TRIG

2ND EDITION

Lloyd Lambert
Laurel Technical Services

Zvonimir Hlousek
California State University, Long Beach

Brooks/Cole Publishing Company

I(T)P® An International Thomson Publishing Company

Pacific Grove · Albany · Belmont · Bonn · Boston · Cincinnati · Detroit
Johannesburg · London · Madrid · Melbourne · Mexico City · New York
Paris · Singapore · Tokyo · Toronto · Washington

For more information, contact:

BROOKS/COLE PUBLISHING COMPANY
511 Forest Lodge Road
Pacific Grove, CA 93950
USA

International Thomson Publishing Europe
Berkshire House 168-173
High Holborn
London WC1V 7AA
England

Thomas Nelson Australia
102 Dodds Street
South Melbourne, 3205
Victoria, Australia

Nelson Canada
1120 Birchmount Road
Scarborough, Ontario
Canada M1K 5G4

International Thomson Editores
Seneca 53
Col. Polanco
11560 México, D. F., México

International Thomson Publishing GmbH
Königswinterer Strasse 418
53227 Bonn
Germany

International Thomson Publishing Asia
60 Albert Street
#15-01 Albert Complex
Singapore 189969

International Thomson Publishing Japan
Hirakawacho Kyowa Building, 3F
2-2-1 Hirakawacho
Chiyoda-ku, Tokyo 102
Japan

Printed in the United States of America

5   4   3   2

ISBN 0-534-35248-0

Table of Contents

CHAPTER 1

1.0 - MULTIPLE CHOICE QUESTIONS

1.   A stere is 1.0 cubic meter of volume. A stere contains:

    a. 1.0×10^3 cm^3
    b. 3.5×10^3 ft^3
    c. 6.1×10^6 cm^3
    d. 1.0×10^9 mm^3
    e.   None of the above

Answer: 1.0×10^9 mm^3

2.   A Norwegian mile is 10.0 km. A Norwegian mile equals how many statute miles?

    a.   1.6
    b.   6.2
    c.   7.8
    d.   16.0
    e.   None of the above

Answer: 6.2

3.   In Scandinavia, compasses are calibrated in grads. 400.0 grads equal 360°. Bergen is about 311.0 grads from Oslo, or:

    a.   226°
    b.   263°
    c.   280°
    d.   300°
    e.   None of the above

Answer: 280°

4.   One pound is equivalent to:

    a.   445 g
    b.   2.2 kg
    c.   18 oz
    d.   4.45 N
    e.   None of the above

Answer: 4.45 N

5.   The acceleration of gravity is approximately 32.2 ft/s^2. This corresponds to:

    a.   7.99 m/s^2
    b.   9.80 m/s^2
    c.   9.81 m/s^2
    d.   9.82 m/s^2

e.   None of the above

6.   An imperial gallon (Canada) is 4.546 liters; it, therefore, corresponds to which of the following U.S. gallons?

      a.   0.95
      b.   1.20
      c.   1.25
      d.   3.8
      e.   None of the above

Answer: 1.20

7.   For precious stones and gems, a measure of mass is the carat. One carat equals 200 mg which corresponds to which of the following ounces?

      a. 7.06×10^{-3}
      b. 3.53×10^{-2}
      c.   28.4
      d. 1.42×10^2
      e.   None of the above

Answer: 7.06×10^{-3}

8.   A wooden dowel has a diameter of 1.5 cm and a length of 10.0 inches. Its volume is:

      a.   0.36 in^3
      b.   3.6 in^3
      c.   7.0 cm^3
      d.   45 cm^3
      e.   None of the above

Answer: 45 cm^3

9.   Density is defined as the mass per unit volume. The density of ice is 0.92 g/cm^3. An ice cube 1.0 inch on a side has a mass of:

      a. 6.6×10^{-2} g
      b.   15 g
      c.   16 g
      d.   5.3 ounces
      e.   None of the above

Answer: 15 g

10.   In Scandinavia, farm size is measured in hectares. 1.0 hectare is 10^4 m^2. 1.0 hectare equals how many acres (1.0 acre = 4840 yd^2)?

      a.   0.4
      b.   2.1
      c.   2.5
      d.   4.0

e.   None of the above

Answer: 2.5

11.   Race horses run distances called furlongs. One furlong is 1/8 mile. A snail might travel a furlong/fortnight or its speed is:

    a. 4.5×10^{-5} ft/s
    b. 5.4×10^{-3} ft/s
    c. 6.0×10^{-4} m/s
    d.   0.17 mm/s
    e.   None of the above

Answer: 0.17 mm/s

12.   Water usage is measured in acre-feet. 1.0 acre-foot is 1.0 acre of water 1.0 foot deep. An acre-foot corresponds to which of the following gallons?

    a. 2.6×10^5
    b. 3.3×10^5
    c. 2.6×10^6
    d. 3.3×10^9
    e.   None of the above

Answer: 3.3×10^5

13.   A cord of firewood is the volume of 2.0 foot long pieces in a stack 16.0 feet long and 4.0 feet high. The number of cords of firewood in a stere (m^3) is:

    a.   0.28
    b.   0.84
    c.   3.6
    d.   10.0
    e.   None of the above

Answer: 0.28

14.   A light-year is the distance light travels at a speed of 3.0×10^8 m/s in 1.0 year. A light-year corresponds to which of the following miles?

    a. 7.94×10^{10}
    b. 8.62×10^{11}
    c. 5.88×10^{12}
    d. 1.52×10^{13}
    e.   None of the above

Answer: 5.88×10^{12}

15.   A water molecule has a mass of 18.0 atomic units. 1.0 atomic unit is 1.66×10^{-24} g. If the density of water (mass/volume) is 1.0 g/cm^3, how many water molecules are in 1.0 cm^3 of water?

    a. 3.4×10^{19}
    b. 3.4×10^{22}
    c. 6.0×10^{23}
    d. 6.0×10^{27}

e.   None of the above

Answer: 3.4×10^{22}

16.   The age of the Universe is estimated to be about 12 billion years. Approximately, how many seconds is that?

    a. 3.8×10^{17}
    b. 8.3×10^{25}
    c. 12×10^{9}
    d. 38×10^{12}
    e.   None of the above

Answer: 3.8×10^{17}

17.   In a very crude approximation a hydrogen atom can be depicted as a sphere of radius 5×10^{-11} m that has a proton at its center. The proton itself can be pictured as a sphere of radius approximately equal to 1×10^{-15} m. How many times is the volume of the hydrogen atom greater than the volume of its nucleus?

    a. 5×10^{4}
    b. 25×10^{8}
    c. 1×10^{14}
    d. 4.3×10^{14}
    e.   None of the above

Answer: 1×10^{14}

1.0 - PROBLEMS

18.   The distance from the center of the earth to the center of the sun is 1.5×10^{11} m. If the diameter of the earth is 1.27×10^{7} m and the sun is 1.39×10^{9} m; (a) Calculate the distance from the surface of the earth to the surface of the sun along a line joining their centers. (b) Calculate the time for sunlight to reach earth in minutes and seconds.

Answer: (a) 1.49×10^{11} m; (b) 8 min, 18 sec

19.   A painter uses a 4.0 inch brush and has an average 24 inch brush stroke while painting; however, he must go over the same area 5.0 times. (a) How many strokes are required to paint a wall 18 feet high and 22 feet long? (b) If each stroke takes an average of 2.0 seconds, how long (hours - minutes) does it take the painter?

Answer: (a) 2970 strokes; (b) 1 hr, 39 min

20.   An ampere of current corresponds to the motion of one coulomb of charge across a surface per second. The electron has 1.6×10^{-19} coulomb of charge. (a) 1.0 ampere corresponds to how many electrons per second crossing a surface? A pen light draws about 5.0 milliamperes of current; (b) How many electrons leave the battery if the pen light is on 40.0 seconds?

Answer: (a) 6.25×10^{18} electrons/s; (b) 1.25×10^{18} electrons

21.   A water pump is capable of pumping 1.5 gallons/minute. How long does it take the pump to empty a circular tank 6.0 feet in diameter and 8.0 feet high that is full of water?

4

Answer: 18 hrs, 48 min

22. A space probe leaves earth at 0.075% of the speed of light for the nearest star (Proxima Centauri) 4.04×10^{16} m away. (a) Calculate the time (in hours and minutes) that it takes for the probe to reach its destination. (b) Calculate the time in days, hours, and minutes.
Answer: (a) 49,876 hrs, 48 min; (b) 2,078 days, 18 hrs, 48 min

23. A person fills an empty 12 gallon tank with fuel at the rate of 3.0 gallons per minute. The tank, however, has a leak and the fuel escapes at the rate of 0.05 liters per second. How long (hours, minutes, seconds) does it take to fill the tank?
Answer: 5 min, 26 sec

24. A workman climbs a cable (hand over hand) at the rate of 1.5 m/s. The cable is on an 18 inch diameter drum which is unrolling the cable at the rate of 50 rpm. How long does it take the workman to move upward 25 feet?
Answer: 25.15 sec

25. On the ocean, distances are measured in nautical miles (6080 feet) which corresponds to a minute of latitude (60 minutes = 1.0 degree). By use of this fact; Calculate the radius of the earth in feet.
Answer: 2.09×10^7 ft

26. The wheel of a car has an outside diameter of 58 cm and is turning at 25 rps. How fast is the car going in mph?
Answer: 102 mph

27. A knot is a nautical mile (6080 feet) per hour. An airplane is flying at 180 mph into a 50.0 kt head wind. Calculate the speed of the airplane over the ground in kph.
Answer: 197 kph

28. The radius of the hydrogen atom can be considered to be 0.53×10^{-10} m in the Bohr model. Suppose we consider these as hard spheres and stack them one on top of the other along a 1.0 inch cube edge to form solid hydrogen. How many hydrogen atoms are there per cubic inch?
Answer: 1.1×10^{26} atoms/in^3

29. A rocket traveling at 800 mph is fired at the tail of a departing aircraft 10.0 km away flying at 650 kt (nautical miles/hour). Calculate the time that it takes the rocket to impact the aircraft.
Answer: 43.5 sec

30. A cow takes a 3.0×1.6 cm strip of grass each bite. A bite and munch takes 12 seconds before the next bite. How long (days, hours, minutes, seconds) does it take the cow to eat 1/10 acre of grass?
Answer: 117 days, 6 hrs, 2 min, 30 sec

31. A town's reservoir fills at the average yearly rate of 6.3 acre-feet per week; whereas, the town uses 1.2×10^6 gallons of water per day. If they start the year with 1000 acre-feet of water in the reservoir, how long (days, hours, minutes, seconds) before they run out of water?
Answer: 359 days, 14 hours, 2 min, 47 sec

32. The earth is divided into 24 time zones corresponding to longitudes that differ by 1 hour in sun time. (a) In the U.S., traveling along the 45° latitude line, how far must you travel (miles) to cross a time zone

5

based on the above definition? (b) On the arctic circle (23.5° from North Pole), how far must you travel (miles) to cross the same time zone?

Answer: (a) 696 mi   (b) 665 mi

33.   A solid cube made of aluminum (density 2.7 g/cm^3) has volume of 0.1 cm^3. How many aluminum atoms are in the cube? (1 mole of aluminum has mass of 27g.)

Answer: 6×10^{21} atoms.

34.   A rectangular plate has length (20.4 ±0.1) cm and width of (9.6 ±0.2) cm. What is the area of the plate?

Answer: (196 ±4) cm^2 .

CHAPTER 2

2.0 - MULTIPLE CHOICE QUESTIONS

1. A ant travels east 12 cm in 16 seconds, north 8 cm in 18 seconds, and southeast 16 cm in 38 seconds. The average speed of the ant is:

    a. 0.5 cm/s
    b. 0.8 cm/s
    c. 1.6 cm/s
    d. 2.0 cm/s
    e. None of the above

    Answer: 0.5 cm/s

2. An erratic fly is tracked by fly radar on the path shown. The average speed of the fly in this 3.0 second interval is:

    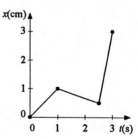

    a. 0.5 cm/s
    b. 1.0 cm/s
    c. 2.0 cm/s
    d. 6.0 cm/s
    e. None of the above

    Answer: 1.0 cm/s

3. An erratic fly is tracked by fly radar on the path shown. The instantaneous speed of the fly at 2.0 seconds is:

    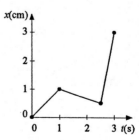

    a. 1/4 cm/s
    b. −1/4 cm/s

c.   1/3 cm/s
d.   −1/3 cm/s
e.   None of the above

Answer: 1/3 cm/s

4.   An aircraft leaves an airport and flies north 50 km then northeast 27 km, and finally south 75 km. The final distance from the airport is:

      a.   10 km
      b.   16 km
      c.   20 km
      d.   24 km
      e.   None of the above

Answer: 20 km

5.   A man walks north 3 blocks (100 m per block) in 4.0 minutes and west 4 blocks in 6 minutes. The man's average velocity magnitude for the walk is:

      a.   0.85 m/s
      b.   1.0 m/s
      c.   14 m/min
      d.   50 m/min
      e.   None of the above

Answer: 50 m/min

6.   A toy boat running through the water at 3.0 m/min goes directly across a stream flowing at 0.24 km/h. The speed of the boat across the river bottom is:

      a.   1.5 m/min
      b.   2.5 m/min
      c.   3.0 m/min
      d.   5.0 m/min
      e.   None of the above

Answer: 5.0 m/min

7.   The sum of three vectors $A_x = 3$, $A_y = 4$; $B_x = 3$, $B_y = -3$; $C_x = -6$, $C_y = -2$ is a vector D, where D_x equals:

      a.   0
      b.   −2
      c.   11
      d.   15
      e.   None of the above

Answer: 0

8.   The sum of three vectors $A_x = 3$, $A_y = 4$; $B_x = 3$, $B_y = -3$; $C_x = -6$, $C_y = -2$ is a vector D, where D_y equals:

      a.   1

b.   −1
c.   2
d.   −3
e.   None of the above

Answer: −1

9.   Vector B is subtracted from vector A where $A_x = 3$, $A_y = 2$; $B_x = -3$, $B_y = 2$ to give a vector C where C_x equals:

a.   0
b.   2
c.   4
d.   6
e.   None of the above

Answer: 6

10.   Vector B is subtracted from vector A where $A_x = 3$, $A_y = 2$; $B_x = -3$, $B_y = 2$ to give a vector C where C_y equals:

a.   0
b.   1
c.   2
d.   4
e.   None of the above

Answer: 0

11.   A vector A, in a Cartesian coordinate system, has a length of 6.0 units at an angle of 60°. The A_x component is:

a.   2.0
b.   3.0
c. $3\sqrt{3}$
d.   4.0
e.   None of the above

Answer: 3.0

12.   A vector A, in a Cartesian coordinate system, has a length of 6.0 units at an angle of 60°. The A_y component is:

a.   2.0
b.   3.0
c. $3\sqrt{3}$
d.   4.0
e.   None of the above

Answer: $3\sqrt{3}$

13.   A vector A, in a Cartesian coordinate system, has the components $A_x = -6$, $A_y = 8$. The length of the vector is:

a.   4
b.   6
c.   8
d.   10
e.   None of the above

Answer: 10

14.   A vector A, in a Cartesian coordinate system, has the components $A_x = -6$, $A_y = 8$. The angle the vector makes with the positive x-axis is:

a.   53°
b.   127°
c.   150°
d.   165°
e.   None of the above

Answer: 127°

15.   How far does a cyclist travel in 4.0 h if his average speed is 11.5 km/h?

a.   46 km
b.   23 km
c.   11.5 km
d.   146 km
e.   None of the above

Answer: 46 km

16.   What is the instantaneous speed of the tip of a sweep second hand that is 2.5 cm in length?

a.   0.13 cm/s
b.   0.26 cm/s
c.   0.39 cm/s
d.   0.52 cm/s
e.   None of the above

Answer: 0.26 cm/s

17.   Members of some species of "bird of prey" can dive with an average speed of 70 m/s. How long does it take a bird to reach the ground if it dives along a 200 m path?

a.   13 s
b.   2.86 s
c.   2.86 cm
d.   14 cm
e.   None of the above

Answer: 2.86 s

2.0 - PROBLEMS

18.   A tortoise creeps along at 2.4 m/min. A hare, racing the tortoise, runs at 0.75 m/s for 1.5 minutes then stops 1.5 hours for a bite of grass. He then lopes along at 1.8 kph for 8.0 minutes to cross the finish line. (a) What was the distance of the race? (b) What was the hare's average speed (m/s)?   (c) Who won?

Answer: (a) 308 m; (b) 5.15×10^{-2} m/s; (c) Hare wins

19.   A plot of distance versus time is shown

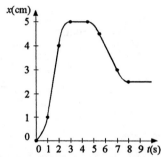

(a) Calculate the average speed for the first 9.0 seconds. (b) Calculate the instantaneous speed at 1.5 seconds. (c) Calculate the velocity at 6.0 seconds. (d) Calculate the velocity at 9.0 seconds.

Answer: (a) 0.28 m/s; (b) 3.0 m/s; (c) -1.0 m/s; (d) 0

20.   The earth rotates on its axis once every 23 hours 56 minutes. The radius of the earth is about 6.38×10^6 m. (a) At what speed would a resident of Salem, Oregon (45° latitude) move relative to the heavens (fixed)? (b) At what speed would an eskimo at the North Pole move?

Answer: (a) 1.18×10^3 km/h;   (b) 0

21.   A person wants to go to the bank which is 1.0 km away in a direction 37° north of east from the person's home. The streets run north - south and east - west only. How many blocks, minimum, must the person walk to get to the bank if a block is 100 m long?

Answer: 7 blocks

22.   Add the three Cartesian coordinate system vectors $A = 4.0$ at 45°, $B = 8.0$ at 150°, and $C = 10$ at 300°. (a) Express your answer in polar form (i.e., magnitude and direction). (b) Express your answer in Cartesian form (i.e., x and y components).

Answer: (a) 2.0 at 296°; (b) $0.90\,\vec{i} - 1.8\,\vec{g}$

23.   A sprinter runs at various speeds along a straight road running northeast. How far does the sprinter go in 16 seconds?

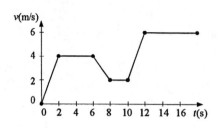

Answer: 62 m

24.   A sprinter runs at various speeds along a straight road running northeast. What is the sprinter's average velocity during the 6.0 second to 8.0 second interval?

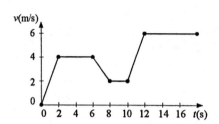

Answer: 3.0 m/s NE

25.   A sprinter runs at various speeds along a straight road running northeast. What is the sprinter's average velocity over the 16.0 second interval?

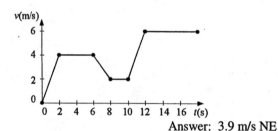

Answer: 3.9 m/s NE

26.   A space station traveling at 1.0 million mph is fired upon by a laser weapon on a space fighter dead ahead 1000 miles away and closing at 2.0 million mph. The space station raises a reflection shield and the laser light is reflected back toward the fighter. Calculate the time after firing for the laser light to return.
                                                          Answer: 10.7 sec

27.   An airplane is to fly due west 280 miles to another airport in 2.0 hours. If there is a 50 kt (nautical miles/hour) north wind; what course and speed must the airplane be flown to make the trip.
                                                          Answer: 292° at 151 mph

28.   While driving southeast at 90 km/h on a straight stretch of road in Texas, a driver notes a hot air balloon passing directly overhead blown by a north wind. 45 minutes later the driver notes the balloon to be on the right side exactly 15° from the road behind. Calculate the speed of the wind in kt (nautical miles/hour).

12

Answer: 14.5 kts

29. Two 10 km marathon runners are 0.5 km apart at the midpoint of the race for the lead runner. The lead runner continues to run at 7.6 kph to the finish line. How fast must the rear runner run to catch up at the finish line?

Answer: 8.36 km/h

30. A passenger plane at the equator flies east at 480 mph. If the earth rotates on its axis once every 23 hours 56 minutes and the radius of the earth is 6.38×10^6 m; calculate the speed of the aircraft (mph) with respect to the heavens (fixed space).

Answer: 1.52×10^3 mi/h

31. A passenger plane at the equator flies east at 480 mi/h. If the earth rotates on its axis once every 23 hours 56 minutes and the radius of the earth is 6.38×10^6 m; calculate the speed of an aircraft (mph) flying west at 480 mph, again, with respect to the heavens (fixed space).

Answer: 561 mi/h

32. An onshore radar station first picks up a ship steaming due west on a bearing of 045°, 6 nautical miles distance. Later the station measures the ship to bear 150°. How far has the ship traveled (nautical miles)?

Answer: 11.6 n.m.

33. In a television tube, electrons are emitted from an electrode at one end of the tube and strike a light-emitting coating on the picture screen at the other end of the tube. If the electrons are emitted with speed of 1.25×10^8 m/s, how long does it take the electrons to hit the screen 16.7 cm away?

Answer: 1.34 ns.

34. Let's say that to get to school you drive 2.2 mi east, then 1.5 mi south followed by 3.7 mi at 45^0 south of east. You make the trip in 20 minutes. What is your average speed?

Answer: 22.2 mi/h.

CHAPTER 3

3.0 - MULTIPLE CHOICE QUESTIONS

1. The region *a* to *b* is parabolic; therefore, the acceleration is:

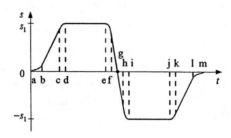

    a.   Increasing
    b.   Constant
    c.   Decreasing
    d.   Zero
    e.   None of the above

Answer: Constant

2. In region *b* to *c*, the acceleration is:

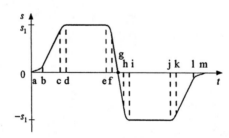

    a.   Increasing
    b.   Constant
    c.   Decreasing
    d.   Zero
    e.   None of the above

Answer: Zero

3. The region *c* to *d* is parabolic; therefore, the acceleration is:

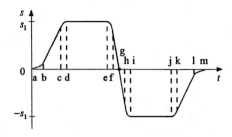

a. Increasing
b. Constant
c. Decreasing
d. Zero
e. None of the above

Answer: Constant

4. In the region *d* to *e*, the speed is:

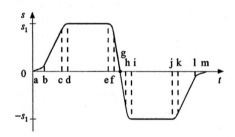

a. Increasing
b. Constant
c. Decreasing
d. Zero
e. None of the above

Answer: Zero

5. The distance traveled, *a* to *m*, is:

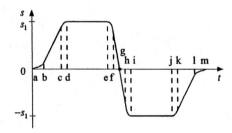

a. Twice the area under the curve *a* to *g*
b. Greater than zero
c. Zero

d. Less than zero
e. None of the above

Answer: Zero

6. The velocity at point *g* is:

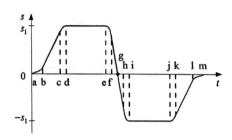

a. Greater than zero
b. Zero
c. Less than zero
d. Cannot be determined from this curve
e. None of the above

Answer: Less than zero

7. In what region is the acceleration largest in magnitude?

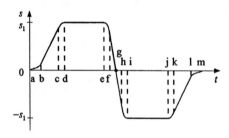

a. *a* to *b*
b. *b* to *c*
c. *c* to *d*
d. *e* to *f*
e. None of the above

Answer: *e* to *f*

8. A bullet is fired horizontally with a muzzle velocity of 400 m/s by a rifleman. The bullet strikes a target 100 m away. Neglecting aerodynamic effects, it hits the target:

a. 4.0 cm below the center
b. 25 cm below the center
c. 31 cm below the center
d. 1.2 cm below the center
e. None of the above

Answer: 31 cm below the center

9.   Two boys are standing on a bridge 10 m above a stream. Boy A throws a rock horizontally at 5.0 m/s at exactly the same time that Boy B drops a rock vertically.

     a.   Boy A's rock strikes the water first
     b.   Boy B's rock strikes the water first
     c.   Both rocks strike the water at the same time
     d.   None of the above

                                        Answer: Both rocks strike the water at the same time

10. A rocket is fired at an angle of 45° above the horizontal and accelerates the projectile at 5.4 m/s^2. The initial magnitude of the vertical acceleration is approximately:

     a.   3.8 m/s^2
     b.   5.4 m/s^2
     c.   6.0 m/s^2
     d.   9.8 m/s^2
     e.   None of the above

                                        Answer: 6.0 m/s^2

11. An object falls from a hovering helicopter and attains a terminal velocity of 50 m/s before striking the lake below. The object then attains a new terminal velocity in water of 5.0 m/s after decelerating uniformly to a depth of 55 m. This water deceleration is:

     a.   5.0 m/s^2
     b.   11 m/s^2
     c.   17.5 m/s^2
     d.   22.5 m/s^2
     e.   None of the above

                                        Answer: 22.5 m/s^2

12. An aircraft flying horizontally at 324 kph drops a wing tank from an altitude of 1653 m. Neglecting aerodynamic effects, the acute angle, measured from the vertical, at which the center of gravity of the tank strikes the level ground is:

     a.   26.6°
     b.   36.4°
     c.   45°
     d.   60°
     e.   None of the above

                                        Answer: 26.6°

13. A torpedo is fired at a speed of 54 kph toward a distant target. After traveling 4.5 km, the torpedo runs out of fuel and decelerates uniformly at 0.5 m/s^2. The time that it takes for the torpedo to stop is:

     a.   9.0 sec
     b.   30 sec
     c.   108 sec
     d.   120 sec
     e.   None of the above

14. A torpedo is fired at a speed of 54 kph toward a distant target. After traveling 4.5 km, the torpedo runs out of fuel and decelerates uniformly at 0.5 m/s^2. The distance of the torpedo from the firing point when it stops (range) is:

    a.   4500 m
    b.   4725 m
    c.   4925 m
    d.   5175 m
    e.   None of the above

Answer: 4725 m

15. A car starts from rest and accelerates at 4.00 m/s^2 through a distance of 20.0 m. How long did it take the car to cover the 20.0 m distance?

    a.   2.95 s
    b.   1.00 s
    c.   7.00 s
    d.   3.15 s
    e.   None of the above

Answer: 3.15 s

16. If a ball is thrown straight upward and is caught 5 s after being thrown, how fast must it have been going when it left persons hand?

    a.   36 m/s
    b.   24 m/s
    c.   9.8 m/s
    d.   5 m/s
    e.   None of the above

Answer: 24 m/s

17. An object passes a point at 2.5 m/s. It then is observed to be 2.25 m away 1.0 second later, 4.0 m away 2.0 seconds later, and 6.0 m away 4.0 seconds later. The following statement is TRUE.

    a.   The acceleration is constant
    b.   The object will stop in 5.0 sec
    c.   The object will end up 6.25 m away from the starting point
    d.   None of the above are true
    e.   All of the above are true

Answer: The object will stop in 5.0 sec

3.0 - PROBLEMS

18. If the maximum acceleration for a rapid transit train is 4.80 km/h/s and the two closest stations are 1.0 km apart; (a) What is the maximum speed (in kph) possible between these stations? (b) What is the minimum time for the trip? (c) What is the average speed (in km/h)?

    Answer: (a) 132.0 km/h; (b) 54.8 s; (c) 65.7 km/h

19. (a) With what speed must a ball be thrown, vertically, to attain a height of 46.0 m? (b) How long will the ball be in the air before returning to the hand? (c) What is the speed of the ball as it is caught?

    Answer: (a) 30.0 m/s; (b) 6.13 s; (c) 30.0 m/s

20. A projectile is fired at an angle of 60° above the horizontal at a speed of 260 m/s. Neglecting aerodynamic effects; (a) What is the maximum height it will attain? (b) What is the time of flight of the projectile? (c) What is the range of the projectile if the terrain is flat?

    Answer: (a) 2590 m; (b) 46.0 s; (c) 5970 m

21. A basketball player tosses a foul shot 2.0 m above the court at an angle of 60° at a basket 4.3 m away and 3.0 m above the court. (a) With what speed must the ball be thrown to make the shot? (b) How long is the ball in the air?

    Answer: (a) 8.2 m/s; (b) 1.1 s

22. A projectile is fired at a muzzle velocity of 50 m/s at an angle, θ_1, less than 45° and then at an angle, θ_2, greater than 45° but in both cases the range is unchanged at 50 m. (a) Find the two angles, θ_1 and θ_2. (b) Find the two corresponding times of flight, t_1 and t_2. (Neglect aerodynamic effects in both cases.)

    Answer: (a) $\theta_1 = 5.65°$; $\theta_2 = 84.35°$; (b) $t_1 = 1.00$ s, $t_2 = 10.15$ s

23. A batter strikes a baseball 1.0 m above the ground at an angle of 30° above the horizontal. If the distance to the center field fence is 125 m and it is 4.0 m high; (a) Find the speed at which the ball must be hit to clear the fence. (b) Find the time for the ball to reach the fence.

    Answer: (a) 38.4 m/s; (b) 3.76 s

24. A Navy destroyer going very slowly drops a depth charge on the midpoint of a 100 m long submarine which is motionless 1000 m below the surface. The submarine immediately accelerates at 1/2 kph/s to a maximum speed of 40 kph as the depth charge sinks to 1000 m at a constant speed of 10 m/s. (a) If the lethal distance of the blast is 600 m, does the submarine escape? (b) What is the distance of the stern of the submarine from the blast?

    Answer: (a) Yes; (b) 617 m

25. A parachutist leaves the jump plane at 3600 m above the ground and free falls for 25 seconds before opening the chute. The jumper decelerates uniformly from the free fall speed of 176.4 m/s to 2.0 m/s with the chute open in a time interval of 5.0 seconds. (a) How long does it take the chutist to reach terminal velocity? (b) What is the rate of deceleration as the chute opens? (c) How high above the ground is the jumper when the chute is completely open? (d) What is the total time for the jump?

    Answer: (a) 18 s; (b) 34.9 m/s^2; (c) 91 m; (d) 76 s

26. A race car accelerates from rest covering a distance of 7.5 m the first second, 10 m during the second time interval of 1.0 second. (a) What is the average speed and uniform acceleration during the first second? (b) What is the average speed and uniform acceleration during the second time interval? (c) What is the average speed and uniform acceleration during these first two time intervals?

    Answer: (a) 7.5 m/s, 13 m/s^2; (b) 10.0 m/s; (c) 8.75 m/s, −6/5 m/s^2, 8.75 m/s^2

27. An aircraft climbing at a speed of 225 kph at an angle of 45° above the horizontal releases a practice bomb (flour sack) at an altitude of 750 m above the ground at a target 800 m away. Neglecting aerodynamic effects; (a) What is the maximum height above the ground attained by the bomb? (b) Does the bomb strike the target? If not, how far does it miss by?

Answer: (a) 850 m; (b) No, 18.6 m short

28. A child at the top of an icy hill 50 m high and 100 m long (constant slope) starts a sled from rest down the hill. Assuming zero friction between the sled and icy snow; (a) What is the acceleration of the sled down the slope? (b) What is the speed of the sled at the bottom of the slope? (c) How long did the descent take?

Answer: (a) 4.9 m/s^2; (b) 31.3 m/s; (c) 6.4 s

29. If the sled in the previous problem hits slushy snow at the bottom of the hill on level ground and stops in 10 seconds; (a) What is the deceleration at the bottom? (b) How far does the sled travel in all? (c) What is the average speed for the entire run?

Answer: (a) 3.1 m/s^2; (b) 256 m; (c) 15.6 m/s

30. You are jogging (walking and running) as follows: walk 120 m at 4.32 km/h, then run 855 m at 17.1 km/h, then walk 180 m at 4.32 km/h, finally run 750 m at 13.5 km/h. (a) How long a time were you jogging? (b) What was your average speed?

Answer: (a) 10.5 min; (b) 3.02 m/s

31. A car is moving with a constant acceleration as it passes two markers 250 m apart in 10 seconds. The speed of the car is 32 m/s as it passes the second marker. (a) What was the speed of the car when it passed the first marker? (b) How far down the test track from the first marker was the car at rest? (c) How long did the test run take to reach the second marker?

Answer: (a) 18 m/s; (b) 231 m; (c) 18.5 sec

32. A space-craft accelerates uniformly from 50 m/s at $t = 0$ to 150 m/s at $t = 10$ s. How far did the vehicle move between between $t = 2.0$ s and $t = 6.0$ s?

Answer: 360 m.

33. An arrow is shot toward a target on a wall 15 m away with a velocity of 30.0 m/s at an angle of 37.0^0 above the horizontal. The arrow is initially 2.00 m above the ground. At what height above the ground does it hit the wall?

Answer: 11.3 m

34. An object is dropped off the railing of a bridge 60 m above a stream and falls into a small can floating down stream at a constant speed. If the can was initially 5.25 m up stream from the point of impact; (a) How long was the object falling? (b) What was the speed of the stream?

Answer: (a) 3.5 sec; (b) 1.5 m/s

CHAPTER 4

4.0 - MULTIPLE CHOICE QUESTIONS

1.   A small marble rolls across the floor at 1.50 m/s and off the top of a flight of stairs with risers 20 cm high and treads 20 cm wide. The step, measured from the top, that the marble will hit is:

    a.   first step
    b.   second step
    c.   third step
    d.   fourth step
    e.   None of the above

                                                    Answer: third step

2.   A 300 g ball is dropped from a height of 90 cm and bounces back up 66 cm. The change in momentum of the ball is:

    a.   0.18 kg m/s
    b.   1.26 kg m/s
    c.   2.34 kg m/s
    d.   2.52 kg m/s
    e.   None of the above

                                                    Answer: 2.34 kg m/s

3.   A man pushes a 10 kg baby buggy up a 30° incline at a constant speed applying a force of 60 N parallel to the slope. The kinetic coefficient of friction is:

    a.   0.10
    b.   0.13
    c.   0.24
    d.   0.33
    e.   None of the above

                                                    Answer: 0.13

4.   A heavy box is on the verge of slipping down an inclined plane which has a static coefficient of friction of 1.33. What is the angle of the inclined plane in degrees?

    a.   33°
    b.   42°
    c.   48°
    d.   53°
    e.   None of the above

                                                    Answer: 53°

5.   Two boys start pulling a 25 kg object down a path. The angle of pull of one boy is 20° from the path at 18 N; whereas, the other boy pulls with a force of 24 N. If the object moves straight down the path, its acceleration is:

a. 0.42 m/s^2
b. 1.2 m/s^2
c. 1.5 m/s^2
d. 2.3 m/s^2
e.   None of the above

Answer: 1.5 m/s^2

6.   A boy on a sled slides down a 40° snow covered hill with a kinetic coefficient of friction of 0.12. The acceleration of the sled is:

a. 0.76 m/s^2
b. 2.3 m/s^2
c. 3.6 m/s^2
d. 5.4 m/s^2
e.   None of the above

Answer: 5.4 m/s^2

7.   A frictionless, weightless pulley is used to connect the motion of two masses as shown. The static coefficient of friction of m_1 and the table is 0.24. If $m_1 = 10$ kg, how large must m_2 be to cause m_1 to start moving?

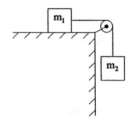

a.   1.2 kg
b.   2.4 kg
c.   4.8 kg
d.   9.6 kg
e.   None of the above

Answer: 2.4 kg

8.   Three masses; $m_1 = 10$ kg, $m_2 = 15$ kg, $m_3 = 20$ kg; are pulled with a force, T_1, of 18 N on a frictionless table. The tension in T_3 is:

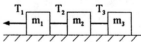

a.   8 N
b.   10 N
c.   12 N
d.   16 N
e.   None of the above

Answer: 8 N

9.   What net force is needed to accelerate a 2,000 kg race car at $\frac{1}{2}g$?
a.   4,600 N

b. 2,400 N
c. 9,800 N
d. 10,000 N
e. None of the above

Answer: 9,8000 N

10. What is the magnifute of the force needed to accelerate a 20 kg cart from rest to 0.50 m/s in 2.0 s?

a. 20 N
b. 5.0 N
c. 9.87 m/s^2
d. 21.0 N
e. None of the above

Answer: 20 N

11. The two ends of a 6.0 kg plank rest on scales. A 4.0 kg mass is placed one-quarter of the way in from one end. The two scales register weights of:

a. 39 N/59 N
b. 40 N/58 N
c. 44 N/54 N
d. 48 N/50 N
e. None of the above

Answer: 39 N/59 N

12. The famous leaning tower of Pisa can be modeled as a uniform cylinder 55 m high and and 7.0 m in diameter. The top is presently displaced 4.5 m from the vertical. The additional top displacement which would cause the tower to topple is:

a. 1.8 m
b. 2.4 m
c. 2.6 m
d. 2.8 m
e. None of the above

Answer: 2.6 m

13. A spherical mooring buoy 36 cm in diameter with a mass of 43 kg is fastened to a cleat on the top of the sea wall by a 50 cm long line, as shown. The force against the sea wall is:

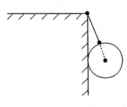

a. 73 N
b. 87 N
c. 104 N
d. 116 N

e.   None of the above

Answer: 116 N

14.   A force of 49 N holds a 15 kg mass by means of a block and tackle system, as shown. The force on the ceiling bracket is:

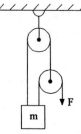

a.   147 N
b.   196 N
c.   294 N
d.   343 N
e.   None of the above

Answer: 196 N

15.   A 4.6 m long diving board of mass of 30 kg is being used by a 60 kg diver standing at the end over the pool. If the board supports are 1.3 m apart, the force on the rear support is:

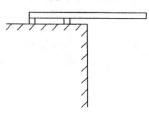

a. 1.2×10^3 N
b. 1.7×10^3 N
c. 2.2×10^3 N
d. 3.2×10^3 N
e.   None of the above

Answer: 1.7×10^3 N

16.   A ladder leans against a slick wall (zero friction) with the foot of the ladder on level ground with a coefficient of friction of 0.06. The greatest angle from the vertical possible without the ladder slipping is:

a.   0°
b.   7°
c.   48°
d.   83°
e.   None of the above

Answer: 7°

17.   A 400 N wieght hangs at rest connected to the ceiling and a nearby vertical wall by two ropes. If the rope connecting the weight to the ceilng makes an angle of 53^0 with respect to the horizontal and the rope

connecting the weight to the vertical wall make an angle of 37^0 with respect to the horizontal what are the tensions in two ropes?

    a.   240 N and 320 N
    b.   512 N and 400 N
    c.   200 N and 200 N
    d.   120 N and 280 N
    e.   None of the above

Answer: 240 N and 320 N

4.0 - PROBLEMS

18.   Three weights of $m_1 = 10$ kg, $m_2 = 15$ kg

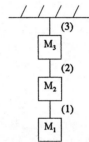

and $m_3 = 20$ kg are suspended as shown. (a) Calculate the tensile force in rope (1). (b) Calculate the tensile force in rope (2). (c) Calculate the tensile force in rope (3).

Answer: (a) 98 N; (b) 245 N; (c) 441 N

19.   Two men are lifting a weight of 1000 kg at a

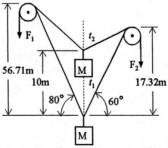

constant speed by use of two pulleys, as shown, for two instants of time, t_1 and t_2. (a) Calculate the forces exerted, F_1 and F_2, by the two men at instant t_1; (b) Calculate the forces exerted, F_1 and F_2, by the two men at instant t_2.

Answer: (a) $F_1 = 7.62 \times 10^3$ N, $F_2 = 8.66 \times 10^3$ N, (b) $F_1 = 2.65 \times 10^3$ N, $F_2 = 2.25 \times 10^3$ N

25

20. An 80 kg sailor in a rope bosun's chair pulls himself aloft by means of a line from the chair to a pulley attached to a yardarm. Neglect the weight of the rope. (a) With what force must he pull to ascend at a constant speed? (b) With what force must he pull to accelerate upward at 0.75 m/s?

Answer: (a) 392 N; (b) 422 N

21. A novice hunter aims his rifle directly at an animal in a 25 m high tree which is 53.6 m away. Just as the hunter fires, the animal falls out of the tree. (a) Neglecting drag, does the hunter bag his game? (b) If the muzzle velocity of the gun is 150 m/s, how long before the bullet reaches the tree? (c) How far has the animal fallen when the bullet reaches the tree?

Answer: (a) Yes; (b) 0.39 s; (c) 77 cm

22. A 112 lb box rests on the floor of a freight elevator which starts from rest and accelerates downward at 4.9 m/s^2 for 5.0 seconds. (a) The force that the box exerts on the floor during the decent is? (b) If the elevator decelerates uniformly to stop in 2.5 seconds, what is the force exerted by the box of the floor during this period of time?

Answer: (a) 56.2 lbs or 250 N; (b) 227 lbs or 1000 N

23. A 170 kg hot air balloon hovers at a constant altitude above the ground. One 70 kg person is in the gondola while another 80 kg person is hanging from a rope ladder below the gondola. The person on the rope ladder starts to ascend at a constant speed of 1.0 m/s. (a) What is the direction and speed of the balloon as he ascends? (b) If the person climbs for 10 seconds then stops, what is the change in the balloon's altitude?

Answer: (a) 0.25 m/s downward; (b) 2.5 m lower

24. A 60 kg delivery man tosses 12 kg boxes to his partner who is 2.0 m vertically above him. The boxes arrive at zero speed as they are caught. The tossing swing takes 0.30 second. (a) What is the acceleration of the box prior to release? (b) What is the force on the ground of the delivery man just as he releases the box?

Answer: (a) 20.9 m/s^2; (b) 838 N

25. Three masses; $m_1 = 10$ kg, $m_2 = 15$ kg,

$m_3 = 20$ kg; are pulled with a force of 166 N across a table with a coefficient of friction of 0.12. (a) Calculate the acceleration of the masses. (b) Calculate the tension, T_2. (c) Calculate the tension, T_3.

Answer: (a) 2.51 m/s^2 (b) 129 N; (c) 73.7 N

26. A box of mass 50 kg slides along a floor

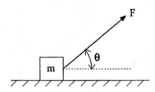

pulled by a force, F, of 175 N at an angle, θ, of 42° as shown. The coefficient of friction is 0.15 between the box and the floor. (a) Calculate the acceleration of the box. If the rope attached to the box breaks after a 1.6 second pull; (b) How far would the box move from its original starting point if it started from rest?

Answer: (a) 1.48 m/s²; (b) 3.8 m

27. A 36 kg sled on the ice of a pond (zero coefficient of friction) has a 48 kg boy on it. The coefficient of friction between the boy and sled is 0.30. Another boy yanks the sled with a horizontal force. (a) Calculate the maximum force that can be applied without the boy sliding off the sled. (b) Find the resulting acceleration of the boy and sled.

Answer: (a) 247 N; (b) 2.94 m/s²

28. A boy swings a 0.50 kg mass on the end of a 4.0 m cord at 45 rpm. (a) Find the tension in the cord. (b) Find the angle the cord makes with the vertical.

Answer: (a) 44.4 N; (b) 6.3°

29. The static coefficient of friction of a block

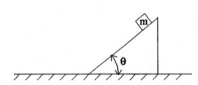

resting on an incline plane is 0.30 and the kinetic coefficient of friction is 0.18. The incline is increased until the block starts to move. (a) Calculate the angle of the incline. (b) What is the speed of the block after traveling 4.0 m to the bottom of the incline? After reaching the bottom it slides across the floor with the same coefficient of friction. (c) How far does it slide on the floor?

Answer: (a) 16.7°; (b) 3.0 m/s; (c) 2.55 m

30. A 1.5×10^4 kg truck pulls a 2.5×10^4 kg trailer on level ground. The friction force of air drag is 150 v Newtons for the truck and 250 v Newtons for the trailer where v is m/s. At an instant the speed of the truck is 45 km/h and the acceleration is 7.2 km/h/s. (a) Calculate the pulling force of the truck. If this is the maximum force available from the truck; (b) calculate the steepest grade the truck and trailer can ascend at 45 km/h.

Answer: (a) 8.5×10^4 N; (b) 12% grade

31. Two boxes are connected by a lightweight cord and a resting on the table. The boxes have masses of 12 kg and 10 kg. A horizontal force of 40 N is applied by a person to a 10 kg box. What is the acceleration of each box?

Answer: 1.8 m/s².

32. A man pushes a 10kg baby buggy up a 30^0 incline at a constant speed supplying force of 60N parallel to the slope. What is the coefficient of kinetic friction?

Answer: 0.13.

33. Suppose you have to hold a mass of 10kg against a wall with a coefficient of friction of 0.70 so that it will not slip down. What must be the minimal force you have to apply?

Answer: 140N

34. A 10 kg box rests on a horizontal floor. The coefficient of static friction is $\mu_s = 0.40$ and the coefficient of kinetic friction is $\mu_k = 0.30$. Determine the force of friction acting on the box if a horizontal external force is exerted on the box and has magnitude of (a) 10 N, (b) 38 N, c) 40N!

Answer: (a) 10 N; (b) 38 N; (c) 11 N.

CHAPTER 5

5.0 - MULTIPLE CHOICE QUESTIONS

1. A TV ad for an automobile showed the car going around a vertical (almost) loop on a vertical loop track. If the diameter of the loop was 36 m, the speed (kph) of the car must have been (to prevent falling at the top of the loop) at least:

    a. 36 kph
    b. 48 kph
    c. 54 kph
    d. 72 kph
    e. None of the above

    Answer: 48 kph

2. An ice skater executes a figure which includes a circle of 4.0 m diameter. If the static coefficient of friction between the skate and the ice is 0.10 during the turn, then the skater's speed cannot exceed:

    a. 1.4 m/s
    b. 2.0 m/s
    c. 2.4 m/s
    d. 3.0 m/s
    e. None of the above

    Answer: 1.4 m/s

3. A cylindrical space station in orbit around earth is to generate artificial gravity for the crew by rotating the cylinder about its axis. If the inside diameter of the cylinder is 50 m, the speed of rotation (rpm) necessary to produce earth's gravity is:

    a. 4.2 rpm
    b. 6.4 rpm
    c. 8.5 rpm
    d. 10 rpm
    e. None of the above

    Answer: 6.4 rpm

4. A person weights 725.2 N on a scale at the equator. This person then travels to Salem, Oregon (45° latitude) and weighs again. If the earth is assumed to be a perfect sphere with $g = 9.8$ m/s^2, radius 6.4×10^6 m, and rotates once every 24 hours, the person would weigh:

    a. 724.4 N
    b. 725.2 N
    c. 725.9 N
    d. 726.8 N
    e. None of the above

    Answer: 725.9 N

5. A plumb bob of 150 g mass is swung in a circular path from a 1.50 m cord. If the diameter of the circle is 60 cm, the tension in the cord is:

    a.   0.8 N
    b.   1.2 N
    c.   1.5 N
    d.   2.4 N
    e.   None of the above

                 Answer: 1.5 N

6. The gravitational force of the earth of mass 5.98×10^{24} kg and radius 6370 km on a 5000 kg satellite 630 km above the ocean is (Newton's constant equals 6.67×10^{-11} m^3/kgs^2):

    a.   8.14 m/s
    b. 4.07×10^4 N
    c. 9.04×10^4 N
    d. 1.24×10^5 N
    e.   None of the above

                 Answer: 4.07×10^4 N

7. Considering the gravitational force of the earth of mass 5.98×10^{24} kg and radius 6370 km on a 5000 kg satellite 630 km above the ocean (Newton's constant equals 6.67×10^{-11} m^3/kgs^2). The acceleration of gravity at sea level on a spherical earth is:

    a. 9.80 m/s^2
    b. 9.81 m/s^2
    c. 9.82 m/s^2
    d. 9.83 m/s^2
    e.   None of the above

                 Answer: 9.83 m/s^2

8. For a spherical earth, the speed of an orbiting satellite in a circular orbit 630 km above the ocean is:

    a.   720 m/s
    b.   7.6 km/s
    c.   7.9 km/s
    d. 8.0×10^5 m/s
    e.   None of the above

                 Answer: 7.9 km/s

9. The moon has a radius of 1.74×10^3 km and a mass of 7.35×10^{22} kg. The acceleration of gravity on the moon is:

    a. 1.62 m/s^2
    b. 1.84 m/s^2
    c. 2.12 m/s^2
    d. 2.86 m/s^2
    e.   None of the above

                 Answer: 1.62 m/s^2

10. Two 80 kg astronauts are in a "weightless" condition in space. If they are 10 m apart, their gravitational attraction is:

   a. 4.3×10^{-8} N
   b. 4.3×10^{-9} N
   c. 5.3×10^{-11} N
   d. 5.3×10^{-12} N
   e.   None of the above

   Answer: 4.3×10^{-9} N

11. The centripetal force on a 500 kg satellite in a stable circular orbit at an altitude of 230 km above the ocean is:

   a.   9.2 N
   b.   27 N
   c. 4.6×10^{3} N
   d. 1.5×10^{12} N
   e.   None of the above

   Answer: 4.6×10^{3} N

12. A satellite in stable orbit 230 km above the ocean has a period of:

   a.   56 minutes
   b.   64 minutes
   c.   73 minutes
   d.   89 minutes
   e.   None of the above

   Answer: 89 minutes

13. The period of the earth's rotation on its axis, relative to the fixed heavens, is 8.62×10^{4} seconds. The altitude of a geosynchronous satellite above the ocean must be:

   a. 1.2×10^{4} km
   b. 1.8×10^{4} km
   c. 3.6×10^{4} km
   d. 4.2×10^{4} km
   e.   None of the above

   Answer: 3.6×10^{4} km

14. If the earth's rotation on its axis has a period of 8.62×10^{4} seconds, relative to the heavens, the speed of a geosynchronous satellite in orbit is:

   a. 1.5×10^{3} m/s
   b. 3.1×10^{3} m/s
   c. 4.2×10^{3} m/s
   d. 1.5×10^{4} m/s
   e.   None of the above

   Answer: 3.1×10^{3} m/s

15. The mass of the moon is 7.35×10^{22} kg and its center to center distance from the earth is 3.84×10^8 m. The earth has a mass of 5.98×10^{24} kg and its radius is 6.37×10^6 m. The gravitational acceleration of the moon on the ocean when it is directly above the ocean is:

    a. 3.22×10^{-5} m/s^2
    b. 3.44×10^{-5} m/s^2
    c. 9.82×10^{-5} m/s^2
    d. 1.26×10^{-4} m/s^2
    e.   None of the above

$$\text{Answer: } 3.44 \times 10^{-5} \text{ m/s}^2$$

16. What is the magnitude of the net gravitational force on the moon ($m_{moon} = 7.35 \times 10^{22}$ kg) due to the gravitational attraction of the earth ($m_{earth} = 5.98 \times 10^{24}$ kg) and the sun ($m_{sun} = 1.99 \times 10^{30}$ kg) when they are at right angle to each other.

    a. 4.79×10^{20} N
    b. 3.21×10^{19} N
    c. 9.82×10^{21} N
    d. 1.26×10^{20} N
    e.   None of the above

$$\text{Answer: } 4.79 \times 10^{20} \text{ N}$$

17. What is the force of gravity acting on a 2,000 kg satellite orbiting the earth in the orbit of radius equal to two earth radii (radius of the earth is approximately 6,380 km).

    a.   36,000 N
    b.   24,000 N
    c.   50,321 N
    d.   19,600 N
    e.   None of the above

$$\text{Answer: } 19,600 \text{ N.}$$

5.0 - PROBLEMS

18. One notes a pelican circling at a constant altitude around a point below in the water. The angle of bank of the pelican relative to the horizontal is 30° and it takes 8.0 seconds for a complete circuit. (a) Calculate the speed at which the pelican is flying. (b) Calculate the diameter of the bird's orbit.

$$\text{Answer: (a) 7.2 m/s; (b) 9.2 m}$$

19. A car goes around an icy turn (zero coefficient of friction) on a highway with a 30° bank. If the radius of the turn is 40.0 m; (a) Calculate the speed (kph) the car must go to avoid slipping (inward motion) or skidding (outward motion). If the coefficient of friction for slipping and skidding is 0.10; (b) Calculate the maximum speed (km/h) without skidding. (c) Calculate the maximum speed (kph) without slipping.

$$\text{Answer: (a) 54 km/h; (b) 59 km/h; (c) 49 km/h}$$

20. A ferris wheel is turning at a constant speed. If you normally weigh 637 N but your apparent weight at the top is 495 N; (a) Calculate your apparent weight at the bottom. If the speed of the ferris wheel is

increased 50%; (b) Calculate your resulting apparent weight at the top. (c) Calculate your resulting apparent weight at the bottom.

Answer: (a) 779 N; (b) 424 N.; (c) 850 N

21. A child swings a 250 g weight on the end of a small string at a constant speed of 96 rpm while letting out the cord. If the string has a tensile strength of 8.5 N; (a) Calculate the length of the string when the string breaks. If the child's hand is 1.25 m above the ground; (b) How far from the child does the weight hit the ground when the string breaks?

Answer: (a) 8.5 N; (b) 1.14 m

22. A 250 g mass, m_2, is rotating at 120 rpm

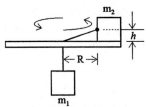

on a table, as shown. Another mass, m_1, is connected to m_2 by a string through a hole in the table. At a particular instant, m_1 is at rest with $R = 37$ cm and $h = 9.0$ cm. (a) Calculate the mass, m_1.

Answer: 300 g

23. A bobsled and crew go around a 5.0 m radius turn measured to the center of the semicircular chute of 2.4 m diameter. When the crew lean 60° away from the vertical; (a) Calculate the speed of the sled. (b) Calculate the centripetal acceleration.

Answer: (a) 10 m/s; (b) 17 m/s^2

24. Two 85.0 kg astronauts are sitting on opposite sides of a cylindrical space station with their center of masses 2.0 m from the axis of the cylinder and on a diameter connecting them through this axis. Calculate the speed of rotation (rpm) necessary to overcome the gravitational attraction between them.

Answer: 1.27×10^{-4} rpm

25. If the earth rotates once on its axis every 23 hours 56 minutes; calculate the minimum density (g/cm^3) that a homogeneous earth must exceed in order to prevent the surface matter from being thrown off into space. ($M = \rho V$.)

Answer: 1.9×10^{-2} g/cm^3

26. A binary star system has stars of mass 2.5×10^{30} kg. The stars are 1.0×10^{10} m apart on orbit around a point called the center of mass midway between them. Calculate the period of their orbits.

Answer: 95.6 hours

27. A spherical planet consists of a dense inner core ($\rho = 7.5$ g/cm^3) of radius 4.5×10^3 km and a less dense outer sheath ($\rho = 2.5$ g/cm^3) of outer radius 13.5×10^3 km. Calculate the acceleration of gravity at the surface.

Answer: 3.84 m/s^2

28. Jupiter (mass 1.90×10^{27} kg) has four moons with the following average radii: Io, 4.22×10^8 m; Europa, 6.71×10^8 m; Ganymede, 1.07×10^9 m; and Callisto, 1.88×10^9 m. (a) Calculate the period of Io. (b)

Calculate the period of Europa. (c) Calculate the period of Ganymede. (d) Calculate the period of Callisto.

> Answer: (a) 1.77 days; (b) 3.55 days; (c) 7.15 days; (d) 16.7 days

29. A satellite is in a stable circular orbit at the equator 650 km above the ocean. (a) Calculate its orbital speed. (b) Calculate its period. (c) Calculate the time it takes for it to return over the same point on earth if it is traveling east.

> Answer: (a) 7.54 km/s; (b) 97.5 min; (c) 104 minutes

30. Three identical planets of 6.0×10^{24} kg mass are located at each of the vertices of an equilateral triangle of side 1.2×10^6 km. (a) Calculate the orbital speed of the planets. (b) Calculate the period of the planets.

> Answer: (a) 578 m/s; (b) 87.25 days

31. A space capsule is at rest relative to a 6.4×10^6 kg space station 8.0 km away. (a) Calculate the acceleration of the capsule due to the space station's gravity. (b) How long would it take the capsule to "fall" 10 m toward the space station?

> Answer: (a) 6.67×10^{-12} m/s^2; (b) 20 days

32. What must be the orbital velocity of a 7,000 kg satellite so that it can stay in a circular orbit 200 km above the surface of the earth?

> Answer: 7.79×10^3 m/s.

33. The period of planet Venus is 225 earth days. Assuming that the orbit of Venus is almost a perfect circle find its distance from the sun (mean distance between the earth and the sun is 1.50×10^{11} m)!

> Answer: 1.08×10^{11} m.

34. A shuttle in orbit around the earth is powered by its rocket motors at an altitude of 800 km and makes an orbit in 120 minutes. (a) Calculate the acceleration of gravity in the shuttle. (b) Calculate the orbit altitude to reduce gravity to zero.

> Answer: (a) 2.3 m/s^2; (b) 1.7×10^3 km

CHAPTER 6

6.0 - MULTIPLE CHOICE QUESTIONS

1. A 500 N box is pushed up a 50° inclined ramp at a constant speed by a horizontal force. The work done after moving the box 5.2 m is:

    a. 1.3×10^3 J
    b. 2.0×10^3 J
    c. 2.4×10^3 J
    d. 3.1×10^3 J
    e. None of the above

    Answer: 2.0×10^3 J

2. A mass is moved in a straight line on a flat surface by a force that varies with position, as shown. The work done to move the mass 8.0 m is:

    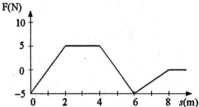

    a. 5.0 J
    b. 10 J
    c. 15 J
    d. 35 J
    e. None of the above

    Answer: 5.0 J

3. A trunk is pulled across a horizontal floor at a constant speed by a 12 N force applied by a rope at an angle of 25° above the horizontal. The work done by friction after moving the trunk 4.0 m is:

    a. 44 J
    b. 48 J
    c. −44 J
    d. −48 J
    e. None of the above

    Answer: −44 J

4. A trunk is pulled across a horizontal floor at a constant speed by a 12 N force applied by a rope at an angle of 25° above the horizontal. If the trunk weighs 90 N the coefficient of friction is:

    a. 0.10
    b. 0.12
    c. 0.15
    d. 0.18
    e. None of the above

5. A 1.6×10^3 kg space probe is launched and achieves escape velocity (11.2 km/s) rapidly using solid fuel rockets. Neglecting loss of mass due to the burning of fuel, the energy that the rockets provide is:

    a. 1.6×10^4 J
    b. 1.8×10^5 J
    c. 2.0×10^9 J
    d. 1.0×10^{11} J
    e. None of the above

    Answer: 1.0×10^{11} J

6. A motorboat engine generates a drive force of 840.0 N resulting in a 20.0 mph speed. The horsepower (1 hp = 746 J/s) of the motor is:

    a. 7.5 hp
    b. 8.2 hp
    c. 10 hp
    d. 12.5 hp
    e. None of the above

    Answer: 10 hp

7. An 80 kg student runs up a flight of stairs to the fifth floor, each floor is 5.0 m above the other, in 28 seconds. The student's horsepower is:

    a. 1/8 hp
    b. 1/4 hp
    c. 1/2 hp
    d. 3/4 hp
    e. None of the above

    Answer: 3/4 hp

8. A sphere rolls without slipping down an incline plane 1.8 m high. Its speed at the bottom is:

    a. 4.0 m/s
    b. 5.0 m/s
    c. 6.0 m/s
    d. 8.0 m/s
    e. None of the above

    Answer: 5.0 m/s

9. A 310 g football of moment of inertia 2.6×10^{-3} kg m^2 and spinning 10 rps travels 5.0 m horizontally in 1.0 second. Its energy is:

    a. 4.0 J
    b. 6.8 J
    c. 9.0 J
    d. 11.6 J
    e. None of the above

10. The acceleration of a 2.6 kg mass increases linearly from zero to 10 m/s^2 over a distance of 12 m. The work done by the accelerating force is:

   a. 60 J
   b. 120 J
   c. 156 J
   d. 312 J
   e. None of the above

Answer: 156 J

11. An Olympic swimmer travels through the water at 1.0 kph in spite of a 90 N drag force. The power of the swimmer is:

   a. 25 J/s
   b. 32 J/s
   c. 45 J/s
   d. 90 J/s
   e. None of the above

Answer: 25 J/s

12. A boy, initially at rest, swings across a 38 m wide stream on a 38 m long rope attached to a limb hanging midway over the stream. The banks on both sides are the same distance above the water. The speed of the boy at his lowest point of the swing is:

   a. 8.0 m/s
   b. 10 m/s
   c. 14 m/s
   d. 18 m/s
   e. None of the above

Answer: 10 m/s

13. A 290 g baseball is thrown from a height of 2.0 m above the ground at a speed of 16 m/s to a height of 9.0 m above the ground with a speed of 10.0 m/s. The work done against gravity is:

   a. 20 J
   b. 28 J
   c. 36 J
   d. 48 J
   e. None of the above

Answer: 20 J

14. A 290 g baseball is thrown from a height of 2.0 m above the ground at a speed of 16 m/s to a height of 9.0 m above the ground with a speed of 10.0 m/s. The work done against air drag is:

   a. zero
   b. −2.7 J
   c. 2.7 J
   d. −4.8 J

e.   None of the above

Answer: −2.7 J

15.   How much work is required to accelerate a 1,000 kg car from 20 m/s to 30 m/s?

    a.   250 kJ
    b.   350 MJ
    c.   15 k J
    d.   123 kJ
    e.   None of the above

Answer: 250 kJ

16.   A car is traveling freely down the slope of the hill which is 40 m high. If the car has started at the top with no speed, at what height above the ground will its speed be one half of the speed at the bottom?

    a.   35 m
    b.   15 m
    c.   20 m
    d.   30 m
    e.   None of the above

Answer: 30 m

17.   A force is applied downward at an angle of 15° above the horizontal to a 12 kg box on a horizontal floor causing it to accelerate at 1.6 m/s^2, even though the coefficient of friction is 0.18. The work done to move the box 6.5 m is:

    a.   120 J
    b.   276 J
    c.   312 J
    d.   327 J
    e.   None of the above

Answer: 276 J

6.0 - PROBLEMS

18.   A 10 kg box is at rest at the top of an incline plane 8.0 m high and 14 m long. The coefficient of friction is 0.20. (a) Calculate the kinetic energy of the box at the bottom of the incline plane. (b) Calculate the work done against friction.

Answer: (a) 559 J; (b) −225 J

19.   A 25 N ball, initially at rest, swings from the horizontal on a 1.0 m cord, as shown, to a full

38

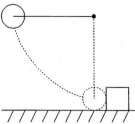

stop at the bottom after striking a 25 N box on a horizontal floor. (a) Calculate the speed of the box after being struck. (b) If the coefficient of friction is 0.25, calculate the work done against friction.

Answer: (a) 4.4 m/s; (b) −245 J

20. A small box slides from rest down a frictionless ramp and around a circular loop as shown.

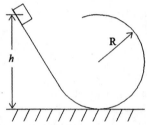

If h is the height of the C.M. above the bottom reference; Calculate the value of h necessary to just keep the box from falling at the top of the loop in terms of its radius R.

Answer: 2.5 R

21. A small sphere rolls from rest down a frictionless ramp and around a circular loop as shown.

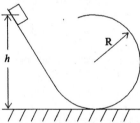

If h is the height of the C.M. above the bottom reference; Calculate the value of h necessary to just keep the sphere from falling at the top of the loop in terms of its radius R.

Answer: 2.7 R

22. Children slide down a frictionless water slide of 12 m height above the deck into a pool 1.2 m below

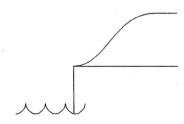

the deck, as shown. (a) Calculate the speed of the children at the bottom of the slide. (b) Calculate the kinetic energy of a 250 N child that hits the water.

Answer: (a) 15.3 m/s; (b) 3.3 × 10³ J

23. A car is stopped, out of gas, at the top of a 850 m hill with a 15° downgrade ahead followed by a 10° upgrade to a 600 m hill before a downgrade to the gas station. The average coefficient of friction is 0.036. (a) Calculate the speed of the car at the top of the second hill. (b) Calculate the maximum coefficient of friction to reach the top of the second hill (full stop).

Answer: (a) 58 km/h; (b) 0.038

24. A block starts up a 30° incline plane at 12 m/s. The coefficient of friction is 0.075. (a) Calculate the distance the block goes up the plane before stopping. (b) Calculate the speed at the bottom as the block slides back down.

Answer: (a) 13 m; (b) 10.5 m/s

25. A cue ball moving at 6.0 m/s strikes two other billiard balls and stops. The two balls rebound at angles 60° above and 30° below the extended track of the cue ball. (a) Calculate the speed of the 60° ball. (b) Calculate the speed of the 30° ball.

Answer: (a) 3.0 m/s; (b) 5.2 m/s

26. A large 290 g ball is thrown vertically upward at a speed of 16 m/s from a height of 2.0 m above the ground. A constant 2.6 N friction force acts upon the ball throughout its flight. (a) Calculate the height the ball attains above the ground. (b) Calculate the speed of the ball as it hits the ground on its return.

Answer: (a) 8.82 m; (b) 3.84 m/s

27. A 50 g rifle bullet is fired into a 7.2 kg mass causing it to swing upward 5.6 cm, as shown.

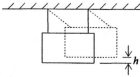

(This is called a ballistic pendulum.) (a) Calculate the speed of the mass immediately after impact by the bullet. (b) Calculate the muzzle velocity of the rifle.

Answer: (a) 1.05 m/s; (b) 152 m/s

28. A 50 g rifle bullet is fired into a 7.2 kg mass causing it to swing upward 5.6 cm, as shown.

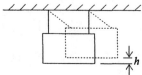

(This is called a ballistic pendulum.) (a) Calculate the kinetic energy of the bullet before impact. (b) Calculate the maximum potential energy of the mass after impact. (c) What percent of the kinetic energy of the bullet is transformed to potential energy?

Answer: (a) 577 J; (b) 3.98 J; (c) 0.69%

29. Two ice skaters collide and hold on to one another for balance. Initially, one 620 N skater, was going south at 5.8 m/s while the other, 760 N skater, was going 30° north of west at 7.2 m/s. Calculate the speed and direction of the skaters after impact.

Answer: (a) 3.49 m/s at 260°

30. Two masses, one 60 kg and the other 40 kg are attached on the ends of a weightless 1.25 m bar

pivoted in the center, as shown. (a) Calculate the angular velocity of the masses after 1/4 revolution if released from rest. (b) Calculate the angular velocity after 1/2 revolution after release.

Answer: (a) 2.5 rad/s; (b) 0

31. A 5.0 kg drum has a weightless cord wrapped around it and a 7.5 N weight attached to the end of the cord. The weight is initially at rest. (a) Calculate the speed of descent of the weight after descending 2.4 m. (b) Calculate the kinetic energy of the system at this instant.

Answer: (a) 3.3 m/s; (b) 18 J

32. Estimate the kinetic energy and the velocity required for a 70 kg pole volter to pass over a bar 5.0 m high. Assume that pole volter's center of mass is initially 0.90 m off the ground and it reaches its maximum height at the level of the bar itself!

Answer: K.E. = 2.8 kJ; v = 8.9 m/s.

33. A 2.6 kg ball, starting from rest, falls a vertical distance of 55 cm before striking a vertical coiled sping, which it compresses. If the spring has stiffness constant k = 720 Nm and negligible mass, what is the maximum compression of the spring?

Answer: 0.24 m

34. The energy stored in a coil spring is $1/2kx^2$ where k is the spring constant (stiffness) and x is the

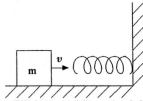

displacement of the spring from its equilibrium position. An 8.0 kg mass moving at 2.5 m/s over a surface with a coefficient of friction of 0.25 collides with a spring of spring constant 600 N/m, as shown. (a) Calculate the maximum energy stored in the spring. (b) Calculate the distance the mass moves on rebound after compressing the spring.

Answer: (a) 22.3 J; (b) 1.14 m

CHAPTER 7

7.0 - MULTIPLE CHOICE QUESTIONS

1. A cue strikes a cue ball exerting an average force of 50 N for 10 ms. If the mass of the ball is 200 g, the speed of the ball after impact is:

   a. 5.0 cm/s
   b. 100 cm/s
   c. 200 cm/s
   d. 500 cm/s
   e. None of the above

   Answer: 500 cm/s

2. A 250 g ball with a speed of 5.0 m/s strikes a vertical wall for 10 ms at an angle of 30° to the surface and rebounds at the same angle with the same speed. The impulse on the ball is:

   a. 1.25 N
   b. 2.5 N
   c. 4.33 N
   d. 5.0 N
   e. None of the above

   Answer: 1.25 N

3. An average force of 2500 N is applied for 1.0 ms to a 10 g bullet moving with a speed of 250 m/s as it passes through a target. The final speed of the bullet is:

   a. zero
   b. 10 m/s
   c. 100 m/s
   d. 225 m/s
   e. None of the above

   Answer: zero

4. Assume the force exerted on a 60 g tennis ball hitting a wall can be represented by the curve shown. If the initial speed of the ball is 25 m/s and it rebounds perpendicularly at the same speed, the maximum force exerted on the ball is:

   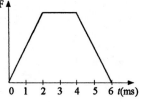

   a. 0.0125 N
   b. 0.375 N
   c. 0.75 N

d. 1.5 N
e. None of the above

Answer: 0.75 N

5. The booster rocket casing of 1500 kg is separated from a 12,000 kg spaceship by explosive bolts. An impulse of at least 480 Ns is needed for safe separation. The speed of the booster casing relative to the spaceship after separation is:

a. 0.04 m/s
b. 0.028 m/s
c. 0.32 m/s
d. 0.36 m/s
e. None of the above

Answer: 0.36 m/s

6. A croquet ball of 0.50 kg mass is struck by a mallet receiving an isosceles triangle shaped impulse with a maximum of 2500 N for 3.0 ms. The final speed of the ball is:

a. 3.75 m/s
b. 7.5 m/s
c. 15 m/s
d. 22 m/s
e. None of the above

Answer: 7.5 m/s

7. A cue ball strikes another billiard ball at rest and goes off at an angle of 60° relative to its extended path at a speed of 4.0 m/s. The struck ball goes off at 6.0 m/s. The angle at which the hit ball moves relative to the extended path of the cue ball is:

a. 35°
b. 42°
c. 58°
d. 65°
e. None of the above

Answer: 35°

8. A cable on a drum is pulling a 12 ton fishing boat out of the water and along a well greased shipway (zero friction) at an angle of 30° to the horizontal at a constant speed of 0.5 fps. The force on the cable is:

a. 3 ton
b. 6 ton
c. 9 ton
d. 12 ton
e. None of the above

Answer: 6 ton

9. A boy weighing 112.5 pounds standing on a 14.06 pound skateboard which is at rest jumps quickly to an identical skateboard ahead which is also at rest with a speed of 2.5 m/s. The speed of the first skateboard after the jump is:

a. 1.5 m/s

b. 8.0 m/s

c. 20 m/s

d. 25 m/s

e. None of the above

Answer: 20 m/s

10. Water leaves a hose at a rate of 1.5 kg/s with a speed of 20 m/s and strikes a wall which stops it (that is, we ignore any splashing back). What is the force exerted by the water on the wall?

a. $-30\,N$

b. $+45\,N$

c. $-45\,N$

d. $+30\,N$

e. None of the above

Answer: $-30\,N.$

11. A 10,000 kg railroad car traveling at speed of of 24.0 m/s strikes an identical car at rest. If the cars lock together as a result of a collision, what is their common speed afterwards?

a. 24.0 m/s

b. 240 m/s

c. 2.40 m/s

d. 12.3 m/s

e. None of the above

Answer: 24 m/s

12. What is the recoil velocity of a $1,000$ kg *cannon* that shoots 10 kg bullets at a speed of 380m/s?

a. -3.8 m/s

b. 4.5 m/s

c. 7.3 m/s

d. -5.4 m/s

e. None of the above

Answer: -3.8 m/s

13. A particle of mass 50g moving with speed of 4.0m/s collides head on with a second particle of equal mass at rest. What are the speeds of two particles after the collision, assuming it is ellastic?

a. 24.0 m/s & 0 m/s

b. 0 m/s & 240 m/s

c. 0 m/s & 4.0 m/s

d. 4.0 m/s & 0 m/s

e. None of the above

Answer: 0 m/s & 4.0 m/s

14. A proton traveling with speed 8.2×10^5m/s collides elastically with a stationary proton in a hydrogen target. One of the protons is observed to be scatterd at a 60^0 angle. At what angle will the second proton be observed?

a. 45^0

b. -30^0

c. -60^0

d. 72^0

e.   None of the above

Answer: -30^0

15.   A 10,000 kg railroad car traveling at speed of of 24.0 m/s strikes an identical car at rest. If the cars lock together as a result of a collision, how much of the initial kinetic energy is transferred to thermal or other forms of energy?

a. 3.00×10^{19} J

b. 2.34×10^{12} J

c. 1.44×10^{6} J

d. 7.19×10^{2} J

e.   None of the above

Answer: 1.44×10^6 J

16.   Consider three particles of equal mass m positioned along the x axis at positions 1.0m, 5.0m and 6.0m away from the origin. What is the position of the center of mass?

a.   4.0 m

b.   9.0 m

c.   1.0 m

d.   3.4 m

e.   None of the above

Answer: 4.0 m

17.   A 11,000 pound aircraft lands on an aircraft carrier and decelerates in a right triangle shaped impulse curve from a speed of 320 kph to rest in 1.1 seconds. The maximum force exerted by the arresting gear is:

a.   17.4 N

b. 2.2×10^5 N

c. 4.0×10^5 N

d. 2.2×10^6 N

e.   None of the above

Answer: 4.0×10^5 N

7.0 - PROBLEMS

18.   A 60 kg space traveler (in outer space) shoves another 80 kg space traveler away. The heavier person travels 60 m in 10 seconds before colliding with a wall. (a) At what speed did the lighter person move? (b) What was the impulse imparted during the shove? (c) What is the impulse on the spaceship due to the person striking the wall? (Does not bounce.)

Answer: (a) 8.0 m/s; (b) 480 Ns; (c) 480 Ns

19.   A helicopter gunship has a gatlin gun capable of firing a stream of bullets at a muzzle velocity of 600 m/s. The bullets have a mass of 0.25 kg each. If the gun brackets fracture under recoil forces in excess of 7.50×10^4 N; (a) What is the maximum rate of fire possible? (b) If the helicopter and crew have a mass

of 5.0×10^3 kg, what is the change in its forward speed when the gun is firing at the maximum rate for 1.0 second (neglect loss of weight of the helicopter due to the bullets fired)?

Answer: (a) 500 bullets/s; (b) 15 m/s or 54 kph

20. A metal gas storage tank explodes breaking into three pieces, two of equal mass and the third twice the mass of the others. The two equal mass parts fly off at speeds of 21 m/s at an angle of 100° between them. (a) What is the angle at which the heavier piece flies off relative to either of the other masses? (b) What is the speed of the heavier piece?

Answer: (a) 130°; (b) 27 m/s

21. Marble size hail stones have a mass of about 0.5 g and can fall at speeds up to 30 m/s. If there are 100 hail stones per stere (cubic meter); (a) What would be the force per square meter (neglecting rebound) exerted by the stones? (b) If the stones rebound at 5.0 m/s, what would the force per square meter be in this case? (c) How high would the stones bounce? (Neglect collisions with other stones.) (d) What would the additional force per square meter be due to the second falling of the rebounding stones?

Answer: (a) 45 N; (b) 52.5 N; (c) 1.28 m(d) 7.5 N

22. In the game of curling a large stone is slid along the ice (zero friction) toward a target (somewhat like bowling). If a 20 kg curling stone sliding at 3.5 m/s strikes another identical stone at rest and causes it to move off along the original stone's path; (a) Calculate the resulting speed of the first stone if the impulse was 1000 N for 50 ms. (b) Calculate the final speed of the struck stone.

Answer: (a) 1.0 m/s; (b) 2.5 m/s

23. A moving 150 g ball is hit by a sticky paddle

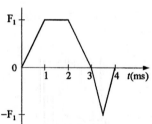

with a maximum force of 1000 N as shown. If the initial speed of the ball was 8.0 m/s; (a) Calculate the speed after being struck by the paddle. (b) At what maximum force would the ball stick to the paddle?

Answer: (a) 2.0 m/s; (b) 800 N

24. A 7000 kg aircraft pops a parachute upon

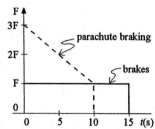

landing to slow in addition to applying constant breaks as shown. The parachute has maximum braking action at the highest speed which is 180 kph and eventually is released by the pilot as the plane slows 10 seconds later as shown. (a) Find the magnitude of the braking force, F, for a full stop. (b) Find the average deceleration during this 15 second time. (c) How far does the aircraft travel during this braking action?

Answer: (a) 1.0×10^4 N; (b) 3.33 m/s^2; (c) 375 m

25. A gun fires a 50 g bullet from a 1.25 m

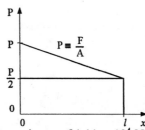

long barrel with a barrel pressure, P, maximum of 1.11×10^4 N/cm^2. The bore of the gun (and bullet) has a cross-section area of 0.15 cm^2. The pressure drops as the bullet progresses down the barrel as shown. (a) Find the muzzle velocity of the gun. (b) Find the impulse on the bullet.

Answer: (a) 250 m/s; (b) 12.5 Ns

26. What is the recoil speed of a 4.0 kg rifle that shoots a 0.050 kg bullet at a speed of 280 m/s?

Answer: 3.5 m/s

27. What is the impulse experienced when a 70 kg person lands on a firm ground after jumping from a height of 5.0 m?

Answer: $-$ 690 Ns

28. Two 69 kg fireman hold a fire hose of 5.0 cm inside diameter which is shooting a stream of water on a fire at the rate of 25 liters per second ($1L = 10^3$ cm^3). Water has a density of 1.0 g/cm^3. (a) Calculate the speed of water leaving the nozzle. (b) If the firemen did not brace themselves when opening the nozzle, at what speed would they recoil backward?

Answer: (a) 12.7 m/s; (b) 2.65 m/s

29. A 50 g bullet traveling at 400 m/s is fired into a 10 kg block resting on level ground with a coefficient of friction of 0.75 between them. If the bullet embeds itself in the block after traveling 25 cm; (a) Calculate the force applied to the block by the bullet. (b) Calculate the velocity of the block as the bullet comes to rest inside it. (c) How far does the block move?

Answer: (a) 1.60×10^4 N; (b) 1.99 m/s; (c) 26.9 cm

30. A proton traveling with speed 8.2×10^5 m/s collides elastically with a stationary proton in a hydrogen target. One of the protons is observed to be scatterd at a 60^0 angle. What will be the speeds of two protons after the collision?

Answer: 4.1×10^5 m/s; 7.1×10^5 m/s

31. A 20 g rifle bullet traveling at 250 m/s burries itself in a 3.8 kg pendulum hanging on a 2.3 m long string. How far does the pendulum swing horizontally?

Answer: 63 cm

33. A ball of mass m makes a head on elastic collision with a second ball (at rest) and rebounds with a speed equal to one third its original speed. What is the mass of the second ball?

Answer: m/2

34. An explosive shell is fired at an angle of 60° to the horizontal with a speed of 200 m/s. At the top of its trajectory it detonates and breaks into two parts; one of which falls vertically downward and has a mass of 1/3 of the other part. (a) Find the time after firing until the detonation. (b) Calculate the distance the second part lands from the first.

Answer: (a) 17.7 s; (b) 2.65×10^3 m

CHAPTER 8

8.0 - MULTIPLE CHOICE QUESTIONS

1.   The angle, in radians, subtended by a quarter coin (2.4 cm diameter) held at arms length (60 cm) is:

      a.   1.1
      b. 2.3×10^{-2}
      c. 4.0×10^{-2}
      d. 4.6×10^{-2}
      e.   None of the above

Answer: 4.0×10^{-2}

2.   The second hand of the clock turns through which of the following radians in 24 hours.

      a.   75
      b. 1.5×10^{2}
      c. 9.0×10^{3}
      d. 5.4×10^{5}
      e.   None of the above

Answer: 9.0×10^{3}

3.   A 24 inch (tire outside diameter) bicycle travels 1/5 mile in 1.0 minute. The tire's angular velocity is:

      a.   4.8 rad/s
      b.   7.2 rad/s
      c.   8.8 rad/s
      d.   17.6 rad/s
      e.   None of the above

Answer: 17.6 rad/s

4.   The bicycle in the previous question, accelerates from rest to 10 mph in 5.0 seconds. The angular acceleration of the tire is:

      a.   1.5 rad/s^2
      b.   2.9 rad/s^2
      c.   4.5 rad/s^2
      d.   6.0 rad/s^2
      e.   None of the above

Answer: 2.9 rad/s^2

5.   A 10 km long, homogeneous pole is placed upright at the equator. Its center of gravity is:

      a.   above the C.M.
      b.   at the C.M.
      c.   below the C.M.
      d.   cannot be found
      e.   None of the above

Answer: below the C.M.

6. Four spherical masses of 1.0 kg, 2.0 kg, 3.0 kg, and 5.0 kg are connected in a line by a weightless rod with center to center distances of the spheres 10 cm. The distance of the C.M. from the 1.0 kg sphere is:

   a. 7 cm
   b. 13 cm
   c. 18 cm
   d. 21 cm
   e. None of the above

   Answer: 21 cm

7. A fisherman reels in his line at the rate of 1.2 m/s on a reel of 5.0 cm diameter using a 7.5 cm long handle. The angular velocity of his hand is:

   a. 24 rad/s
   b. 48 rad/s
   c. 72 rad/s
   d. 96 rad/s
   e. None of the above

   Answer: 48 rad/s

8. A 120 N weight is suspended from a 8.0 kg cylindrical drum of 40 cm diameter, as shown. The angular acceleration of the drum in rad/s^2 is:

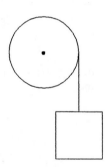

   a. 12.5
   b. 25
   c. 50
   d. 75
   e. None of the above

   Answer: 50

9. A 120 N weight is suspended from a 8.0 kg cylindrical drum of 40 cm diameter, as shown. The weight starts from rest and descends 20 m. The time required for this descent is:

51

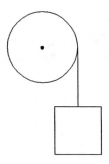

a. 1.4 seconds
b. 2.0 seconds
c. 4.0 seconds
d. 2π seconds
e. None of the above

Answer: 2.0 seconds

10. A cylinder of 50 cm diameter rolls without slipping down an inclined plane. The ratio of the speed of the axis of the cylinder to its angular velocity is:

a. $2\pi/25$
b. 2π
c. 25π
d. 25
e. None of the above

Answer: 25

11. Two 2.5 kg spherical weights of 50 cm diameter are connected by a weightless rod 75 cm, center to center, and revolved about an axis through one of the spheres and normal to the axis of the rod. The moment of inertia of the system is:

a. 0.22 kg m^2
b. 1.5 kg m^2
c. 2.4 kg m^2
d. 6.8 kg m^2
e. None of the above

Answer: 1.5 kg m^2

12. A phonograph record is rotating at 33 1/3 rpm. The drive is disconnected and two identical records are dropped on top. The speed of rotation now is:

a. 33 1/3 rpm
b. 27 7/9 rpm
c. 16 2/3 rpm
d. 11 1/9 rpm
e. None of the above

Answer: 11 1/9 rpm

13. An astronaut in space swings a weight on the end of a 1.25 m thin cord in a circular path increasing its speed by 2.4 rps each second. The tangential acceleration is:

   a.   4.0 m/s²
   b.   4π m/s²
   c.   5.0 m/s²
   d.   6π m/s²
   e.   None of the above

   Answer: 6π m/s²

14. An astronaut in space swings a weight on the end of a 1.25 m thin cord in a circular path increasing its speed by 2.4 rps each second. The radial acceleration of the weight 4.0 seconds after starting from rest is:

   a. $25\pi^2$ m/s²
   b. $360\pi^2$ m/s²
   c. $720\pi^2$ m/s²
   d. $750\pi^2$ m/s²
   e.   None of the above

   Answer: $720\pi^2$ m/s²

15. A centrifuge rotor is accelerated from rest to 20,000 rpm in 3.0 min. What is the average angular acceleration?

   a.   7.0 rad/s².
   b.   7.1 rad/sˢ.
   c.   6.9 rad/sˢ.
   d.   6.8 rad/s²
   e.   None of the above

   Answer: 7.0 rad/s²

16. A 15.0 N force is applied to a cord wrapped around a wheel of mass 4.00 kg and radius 33.0 cm. The wheel is observed to accelerate uniformly from rest to reach an angular speed of 30.0 rad/s in 3.00 s. If there is frictional torque of 1.10 Nm, what is the moment of inertia of the wheel?:

   a.   0.483 kg m².
   b.   0.385 kg m².
   c.   0.283 kg m²
   d.   0.395 kg m²
   e.   None of the above

   Answer: 0.385 kg m².

17. An old gas caterpillar was started by inserting a 90 cm bar into a shallow hole of a 735 N cylindrical flywheel 80 cm in diameter and applying a normal force at 5.0 cm in from the end of the bar to rotate the flywheel from rest to 1.5 rps in 0.15 seconds. The force required was:

   a. 2.3×10^2 N
   b. 3.0×10^2 N
   c. 4.6×10^2 N
   d. 6.0×10^2 N

e.   None of the above

Answer: 3.0×10^2 N

8.0 - PROBLEMS

18.   A wheel of complicated geometry is accelerated from rest to 26 rpm in 8.5 seconds by a 320 N force applied at the periphery 25 cm from its axle. (a) Calculate its moment of inertia. (b) Calculate the number of revolutions made in 8.5 seconds.

Answer: (a) 250 kg m^2; (b) 1.84 rev

19.   A 250 kg satellite is in circular orbit at 250 km over earth. (a) Calculate the angular momentum of the satellite. (b) Calculate its moment of inertia.

Answer: (a) 1.28×10^{13} kg m/s^2; (b) 1.10×10^{16} kg m^2

20.   A majorette throws her baton, which is 1.0 m long and weighs 19.6 N, into the air. It makes 5.0 complete revolutions and returns to her hand 2.0 seconds later.   (a) Calculate its angular momentum in the air. (b) Calculate the height from which it was thrown.

Answer: (a) 2.62 kg m/s^2; (b) 4.9 m

21.   A double cylindrical drum system of radii

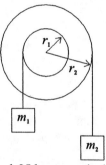

10 cm and 20 cm with masses 15 kg and 25 kg respectively as shown have two weights of 250 N (smaller drum) and 120 N (larger drum) suspended by a weightless cord. (a) Calculate the moment of inertia of the system. (b) Calculate the magnitude and direction of angular acceleration.

Answer: (a) 0.575 kg m^2; (b) 1.24 rad/s^2 $-$ counterclockwise

22.   A uniform rod 2.4 m long and of 5.0 kg mass rotates about an axis perpendicular to it and 1/4 the way in from one end. (a) Calculate the rotational moment of inertia. At one instant of time, it is rotating at 5.0 rps. After 36 revolutions, it is rotating at 8.0 rps. (b) Calculate its angular acceleration. (c) Calculate the time for these 36 revolutions.

Answer: (a) 4.2 kg m^2; (b) 3.40 rad/s^2; (c) 5.54 sec

23.   A phonograph turn table, 36 cm diameter and 6.0 kg mass, is belt driven by a 2.0 cm diameter drive motor capstan. (a) Calculate the angular velocity of the capstan in order to spin the turn table at 33 1/3 rpm. (b) Calculate the torque exerted by the capstan to bring the turn table up to speed in 3 1/3 seconds. (c) Calculate the rotational force the capstan exerts on the belt during this angular acceleration.

54

Answer: (a) 62.8 rad/s; (b) 0.10 N m; (c) 10 N

24. A 0.75 kg meter stick is used as a beam balance with a 2.5 kg mass at 0 mark on the left end, a 1.5 kg mass at the 100 mark on the right end, and the pivot at the 35 mark. (a) Calculate the magnitude and direction of angular acceleration as the stick is released from horizontal. (b) Calculate the angular acceleration after tilting 30°.

Answer: (a) 2.14 rad/s² – clockwise; (b) 1.85 rad/s²

25. A 14 cm diameter sphere rolls without slipping down a 30° incline plane. (a) Calculate the acceleration of the sphere's C.M. (b) Calculate the angular velocity of the sphere after rolling from rest 7.0 m down the incline plane.

Answer: (a) 3.5 m/s²; (b) 100 rad/s

26. A yo-yo has a thin string wrapped around

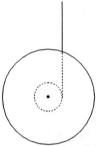

an inner cylinder of about 5.0 mm diameter, as shown. If the yo-yo descends from rest 60 cm in 2.0 seconds; (a) Calculate the acceleration of the C.M. (b) Find the tension in the cord if the yo-yo weighs 1.98 N. (c) Calculate the yo-yo's moment of inertia.

Answer: (a) 0.30 m/s²; (b) 1.92 N; (c) 4.0 × 10⁻⁵ kg m²

27. An anemometer consists of four hemispherical shells of mass 250 g per hemisphere and diameter of 8.0 cm. The center of the hemisphere is 20 cm from the axis of the rotating shaft. (a) Neglect the mass of the connecting arms and shaft, and calculate the anemometer's moment of inertia. (b) Assume the wind acts normal to one hemisphere at a time (effectively) and calculate the wind force necessary to accelerate the anemometer from rest to 120 rpm in 8.0 seconds.

Answer: (a) 4.18 × 10⁻² kg m²; (b) 0.32 N

28. A propeller on an airplane can be modeled as a 2.0 m rod rotated at its center and weighing 160 N. The airplane itself can be modeled as two independent cylinders, the fuselage 1.2 m in diameter and weighing 4000 N and the wings 10 m long and weighing 1000 N. If the propeller is rotating at 2400 rpm and the wing cylinder axis is 1.0 m above the fuselage and propeller axis; (a) Calculate the angular momentum of the propeller. (b) If the propeller starts from zero up to the 2400 rpm speed, calculate the rotation of the airplane in rpm. (c) The propeller rotates clock-wise, as viewed by the pilot, which way does the airplane rotate?

Answer: (a) 1.37 × 10³ kg m/s²; (b) 14.9 rpm; (c) counterclockwise

29. A cylinder and a sphere of different diameters are released from rest at the top of a 45° inclined plane 5.0 m in length. (a) Calculate the speed of the cylinder at the bottom. (b) Calculate the speed of the sphere at the bottom. (c) Which arrives at the bottom first?

55

30. A 2.0 kg hollow sphere is filled with 1.5 kg of sand which leaks out at the rate of 50 g/s. The sphere is rotated in a circle at 75 rpm and is 2.0 m from the axis of rotation. (a) Calculate the angular momentum at time zero before the sand leaks out. (b) Calculate the angular velocity when half the sand has leaked out. (c) Calculate the angular acceleration during this time.

Answer: (a) 110 kg m/s^2; (b) 10 rad/s; (c) -0.143 rad/s

31. A mass m attached to the end of a string revolves in a circle on a frictionless tabletop. The other end of the string passes through a hole in the table. Initially, the ball rotates with a speed $v_1 = 2.4$ m/s in a circle of radius $r_1 = 0.80$ m. The string is then pulled slowly through a hole so that the radius is reduced to $r_2 = 0.48$ m. What is the speed v_2, of the mass now?

Answer: $v_2 = 4.0$ m/s.

32. Two particles of mass 5.0 kg and 7.0 kg, are mounted 4.0 m apart on the ends of a light rod whose mass can be ignored. What is the moment of inertia of the system when it is rotated about an axis passing halfway between masses?

Answer: 48 kg m^2

33. The water molecule, H$_2$O, has a bond angle, θ,

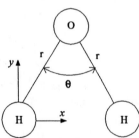

of 104.5° and a bond length, r, of 0.9580Å. The weight of the oxygen atom in atomic mass units (amu) is 16.0000 and hydrogen 1.0079. (a) Calculate the C.M. (Cartesian coordinates) in Å units of H$_2$O. (b) Calculate the moment of inertia (normal to the plane of H$_2$O) in amu - Å^2 units.

Answer: (a) (0.7575 , 0.5209); (b) 0.7526

34. An irregular shaped body is acted upon by

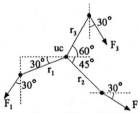

three forces as shown, $F_1 = 120$ N, $r_1 = 12$ cm; $F_2 = 200$ N, $r_2 = 10$ cm; $F_3 = 360$ N, $r_3 = 16$ cm, and the moment of inertia is 1.2 kgm^2. (a) Calculate the torque (magnitude and direction) acting on this body. (b) Calculate the angular acceleration of the body.

Answer: (a) 56.7 N m $-$ counterclockwise; (b) 47.3 rad/s^2

CHAPTER 9

9.0 - MULTIPLE CHOICE QUESTIONS

1.   Hydrogen peroxide (H_2O_2) is a rocket fuel. 340 g of hydrogen peroxide contains which of the following grams of oxygen?

      a.   20
      b.   160
      c.   320
      d.   340
      e.   None of the above

Answer: 320

2.   Four liters of methanol (CH_3OH) ($\rho = 0.79$ g/cm^3) is burned as a fuel. How many liters of water does it produce?

      a.   0.50
      b.   0.79
      c.   1.26
      d.   1.58
      e.   None of the above

Answer: 1.58

3.   Most liquids have about 3.3×10^{22} molecules/cm^3. The weight of a liter of hydrogen peroxide (H_2O_2) would be:

      a.   0.875 kg
      b.   0.985 kg
      c.   1.86 kg
      d.   2.48 kg
      e.   None of the above

Answer: 1.86 kg

4.   A copper BB is about 1.5 mm in diameter. The atomic mass of copper is 63u and the density of copper is 8.9 g/cm^3. The number of atoms in a BB is:

      a. 1.5×10^{20}
      b. 6.3×10^{22}
      c. 1.5×10^{23}
      d. 6.0×10^{23}
      e.   None of the above

Answer: 1.5×10^{20}

5.   Iron (Fe) crystallizes into cubes 2.87Å ($1\overset{\circ}{A} = 10^{-10}$m) on an edge and contains two atoms. The atomic mass of Fe is 56u. The density of Fe is:

      a.   2.50 g/cm^3

b.   7.56 g/cm^3
c.   7.86 g/cm^3
d.   7.92 g/cm^3
e.   None of the above

Answer: 7.86 g/cm^3

6.   A weightless spherical balloon is filled with gasoline ($\rho = 0.80$ g/cm^3) and is placed in seawater ($\rho = 1.025$ g/cm^3). The balloon has which of the following percent of its volume under water?

a.   60%
b.   68%
c.   72%
d.   78%
e.   None of the above

Answer: 78%

7.   A water filled U-tube has oil ($\rho = 0.92$ g/cm^3) poured in one leg to a height of 10 cm. The height difference between the surfaces of the water and oil in the two legs is:

a.   7.6 mm
b.   8.0 mm
c.   8.5 mm
d.   12.5 mm
e.   None of the above

Answer: 8.0 mm

8.   A water filled U-tube has an unknown fluid poured into one arm. The water rises 10 cm in the other arm but still is 2.6 cm below the level of the surface of the unknown fluid whose density is:

a.   0.74 g/cm^3
b.   0.76 g/cm^3
c.   0.79 g/cm^3
d.   1.26 g/cm^3
e.   None of the above

Answer: 0.79 g/cm^3

9.   A two piston hydraulic lift has a 100 N force, F_1, applied to a 5.0 cm diameter piston, as shown, and the corresponding 40 cm diameter piston experiences a force, F_2, of:

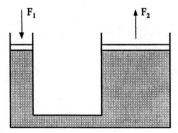

a. 6.4×10^3 N

b. 8.0×10^2 N
c. 3.2×10^2 N
d. 100 N
e. None of the above

Answer: 6.4×10^3 N

10. A thin walled cylinder of negligible weight 5.0 cm in diameter and 10 cm high is loaded with glass marbles ($\rho = 2.5$ g/cm^3) 1.0 cm in diameter until the cylinder sinks in water. The minimum number of marbles required is:

   a. 100
   b. 125
   c. 150
   d. 175
   e. None of the above

Answer: 150

11. An irregularly shaped object weighs 245 N more in air than it does completely submerged in water. Its volume, therefore, is:

   a. 1.8×10^{-2} m^3
   b. 2.5×10^{-2} m^3
   c. 5.0 m^3
   d. 12.5 m^3
   e. None of the above

Answer: 2.5×10^{-2} m^3

12. An irregularly shaped object weighs 245 N more in air than it does completely submerged in water and is 100% iron ($\rho = 7.9$ g/cm^3), then its weight in air must be:

   a. 1.9×10^3 N
   b. 2.5×10^4 N
   c. 3.9×10^5 N
   d. 4.8×10^5 N
   e. None of the above

Answer: 1.9×10^3 N

13. A 1/2 inch (inside diameter) garden hose is connected to a sprinkler head with 80 holes 1.2 mm in diameter. If the water in the hose is traveling at 3.6 m/s, the water leaving the sprinkler head has a speed of:

   a. 0.36 m/s
   b. 1.2 m/s
   c. 5.0 m/s
   d. 9.4 m/s
   e. None of the above

Answer: 5.0 m/s

14. A large open water tank 2.0 m high has a 2.5 inch (ID) output line and a valve 16 cm from the bottom of the tank. The number of gallons of water per minute leaving the tank (1 gallon = 231 in^3) is:

a. 23
b. 3.0×10^2
c. 6.4×10^2
d. 9.2×10^2
e. None of the above

Answer: 3.0×10^2

15. The surface of the water in a storage tank is 30m above a water faucet in the kitchen of a house. What is the water pressure at the faucet?

a. 2.8×10^5 Pa
b. 2.9×10^5 Pa
c. 2.7×10^5 Pa
d. 2.6×10^5 Pa
e. None of the above

Answer: 2.9×10^5 Pa

16. A 70 kg rock lies at the bottom of a lake. Its volume is 3.0×10^4 cm^3. How much force is needed to lift it?

a. 300 N
b. 290 N
c. 280 N
d. 310 N
e. None of the above

Answer: 290 N

17. Air ($\rho = 1.2 \times 10^{-3}$ g/cm^3) flows through a venturi meter using a mercury manometer ($\rho = 13.6$ g/cm^3) to measure pressure, as shown. If the intake diameter is 4.0 cm, the intake air speed is 1.8 m/s, and the neck diameter is 0.50 cm, the height, h, of the mercury column is:

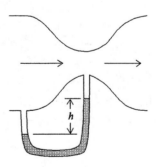

a. 6.0 cm
b. 7.2 cm
c. 7.8 cm
d. 8.6 cm
e. None of the above

Answer: 6.0 cm

18. Two metals, one of density 2.7 g/cm^3 the other 4.5 g/cm^3, are alloyed and form a cube 2.0 cm on a side of weight 0.30 N. Calculate the percentage, by weight, of the lighter constituent.

    Answer: 37%

19. Two moles of acetylene (C_2H_2) burns by combining with 5 moles of oxygen to form 4 moles of CO_2 and 2 moles of water vapor. Calculate the number of liters (STP) of CO_2 by burning 200 g of C_2H_2.

    Answer: 345 L

20. A cylinder 10 cm in diameter has a weightless

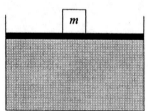

    movable piston 20 cm from the bottom. The gas contained is at STP. A mass of 12 kg is placed on top of the piston. (a) Calculate the final pressure of the gas. (b) Calculate the final distance the piston is from the bottom.

    Answer: (a) 1.16×10^5 Pa; (b) 17.4 cm

21. A sealed cylindrical tin can ($\rho = 5.7$ g/cm^3) has walls 1.0 mm thick and an outside diameter of 5.0 cm and height 10 cm. Calculate the volume of the can that is above the water. The can is filled with air ($\rho = 1.2 \times 10^{-3}$ g/cm^3).

    Answer: 87.8 cm^3

22. A very large open water tank has a 50 cm diameter output pipe connected 10 m above the water main which is 6.0 cm in diameter. The tank supplies water at a speed of 0.5 m/s. Calculate the gauge pressure in the water main.

    Answer: 9.8×10^4 Pa

23. An object weighs 50 N in air and 30 N when immersed completely in water. When completely immersed in another fluid, it weighs 34 N. (a) Calculate the density of the object material. (b) Calculate the density of the fluid.

    Answer: (a) 2.5 g/cm^3; (b) 0.80 g/cm^3

24. A hollow sphere of 13 cm outside diameter and 11.5 cm inside diameter floats with 4/5 of its volume submersed in water. (a) Calculate the mass of the sphere. (b) Calculate the density of the sphere material.

    Answer: (a) 0.92 kg; (b) 2.6 g/cm^3

25. Tom Sawyer decides to make a raft of 6 inch diameter logs 6 feet long ($\rho = 0.50$ g/cm^3) for Huck and himself, who each weigh about 140 pounds. Calculate the minimum number of logs required for them to stay afloat.

Answer: 8

26. A fishing boat captain decides to pump the water from the bilges. His pump delivers 60 liters/minute through a 2.5 cm (inside diameter) hose to the deck 3.0 m above. (a) Calculate the mass flow rate (kg/s). (b) Calculate the power supplied by the pump.

Answer: (a) 1.0 kg/s; (b) 31.5 J/s

27. The top of an aircraft wing of 20 m^2 area measures 1.4 m from leading to trailing edge; whereas, the bottom measures 1.2 m. For laminar flow, the air must travel faster over the top. Calculate the airspeed (kph) necessary for a 7200 N airplane (with passengers) to maintain a constant altitude when the air density is 0.85×10^{-3} g/cm^3.

Answer: 174 km/h

28. A dam filled with water has an output pipe 10 cm inside diameter located 10 m below the surface of the water. (a) Calculate the speed of the water in the pipe with the valve full open. (b) Calculate the number of gallons/hour released with the valve full open. (1 gallon = 3.785 liters.)

Answer: (a) 14 m/s; (b) 1.0×10^5 gal/h

29. A closed cylindrical tank 50 m tall and 10 m in diameter contains benzene ($\rho = 0.88$ g/cm^3) under a pressure of 10 atm and a surface level 5.0 m below the top of the tank. A safety valve opens venting benzene through a 1.0 inch (ID) drain pipe at the bottom of the tank. Calculate the liters/hour of benzene draining from the tank when it is down to half full.

Answer: 8.8×10^4 l/h

30. Alcohol ($\rho = 0.79$ g/cm^3) is passed through a venturi tube with a mercury ($\rho = 13.6$ g/cm^3) manometer for measuring pressure difference. The venturi has a 3.6 cm input port diameter and a 0.60 cm throat diameter. If the mercury manometer indicates 80 torr, calculate the input port fluid speed.

Answer: 14.4 cm/s

31. A marker balloon 20 cm in diameter and weighing 1.8 N (air filled) breaks loose and ascends to the surface of the ocean from a wreck it was attached to at 100 m depth. The drag force during ascent is $F_D = \rho A v^2$ where ρ is the density of seawater (1.025 g/cm^3) and A is the cross-section area in direction of motion. Neglecting changes in the elastic force during expansion, calculate the speed of the balloon as it reaches the surface.

Answer: 1.7 m/s

32. A pitot tube is used to measure the airspeed

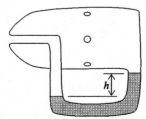

of airplanes and can be seen attached to the leading edge of wings. It consists of a center opening in which the air is not moving and small holes along the sides exposed to the air ($\rho = 1.2 \times 10^{-3}$ g/cm^3) in motion at the speed of the aircraft. Suppose a mercury manometer ($\rho = 13.6$ g/cm^3) is used, as shown, to measure pressure and indicates 11.25 torr. Using Bernoulli's equation, calculate the speed of the aircraft.

Answer: 180 km/h

33. A simple geological model considers a continent as a block (density 2,800 kg/m^3) floating in the mantle rock around it (density 3,300 kg/m^3). Assuming that the continent is 35 km thick (the average thickenss of earth's crust), estimate the height of the continent above the surrounding rock!

Answer: 5.3 km

34. A 30 cm $\times$ 60 cm sign weighing 30 N is hinged at the top. During a hurricane, the wind speed reached 115 kph. Calculate the angle the sign makes with the vertical if the wind speed over the top of the sign is about 10% more.

Answer: 40°

CHAPTER 10

10.0 - MULTIPLE CHOICE QUESTIONS

1.   A coil spring is lengthened 2.5 cm when a 100 g weight is attached. The spring constant is:

      a.   0.39 N/cm
      b.   4.0 N/cm
      c.   120 N/cm
      d.   390 N/cm
      e.   None of the above

          Answer: 0.39 N/cm

2.   A spring with a 49 N/m spring constant has a 250 g weight attached. The spring stores which of the following tensile energies:

      a. 2.0×10^{-2} J
      b. 6.1×10^{-2} J
      c. 12×10^{-2} J
      d.   25 J
      e.   None of the above

          Answer: 6.1×10^{-2} J

3.   The yield point of steel is about 2.5×10^8 N/m^2. A chain with 1.0 cm^2 cross-sectional area links can lift a maximum load of:

      a. 5.0×10^3 N
      b. 2.5×10^4 N
      c. 5.0×10^4 N
      d. 2.5×10^5 N
      e.   None of the above

          Answer: 5.0×10^4 N

4.   A 2.0 N force is applied to the 200 cm^2 surface of the top of a 2.5 cm thick book laying on a table. The top cover is displaced 5.0 mm with respect to the bottom cover. The shear modulus of the book is:

      a.   250 N/m^2
      b.   400 N/m^2
      c.   500 N/m^2
      d.   1000 N/m^2
      e.   None of the above

          Answer: 500 N/m^2

5.   The compressibility (reciprocal of bulk modulus) for the metal sodium (Na) is 14.7×10^{-11} m^2/N. If a cube of Na is subjected to a hydrostatic pressure of 10^8 Pa, the percent decrease in volume is:

      a.   0.72

b. 0.84
c. 1.2
d. 1.5
e. None of the above

Answer: 1.5

6. A 2.4 kg mass is placed on top of a vertical spring. The spring is compressed 4.2 cm. The energy stored in the spring is:

   a. 0.49 J
   b. 0.99 J
   c. 1.2 J
   d. 2.4 J
   e. None of the above

Answer: 0.99 J

7. A torsion pendulum twists through an angle of 18° from equilibrium when a 0.25 N force is applied 1.0 cm from the axis of the wire. The torsion spring constant is:

   a. 0.42 Nm
   b. 0.80 Nm
   c. 1.4×10^{-2} Nm
   d. 8.0×10^{-3} Nm
   e. None of the above

Answer: 8.0×10^{-3} Nm

8. By analogy with the spring, the torsion wire of spring constant 0.075 Nm stores which of the following energies when twisted through an angle of 30°?

   a. 1.0×10^{-3} J
   b. 1.0×10^{-2} J
   c. 2.0×10^{-2} J
   d. 4.0×10^{-2} J
   e. None of the above

Answer: 2.0×10^{-2} J

9. A 1.60 m long piano wire has diameter of 0.20 cm. How great is the tension if it stretches 0.30 cm when tightened? (Young modulus of steel is 2.0×10^{11} N/m².)

   a. 1,200 N
   b. 1,111 N
   c. 1,254 N
   d. 2,040 N
   e. None of the above

Answer: 1,200 N

10. An iron bolt is used to to connect two iron plates together. The bolt must withstand shear forces up to about 2,000 N. What is the minimum diameter of the bolt, based on the safety factor of 7.0! (Shear sterngth of cast iron is 1.70×10^8 N/m².)

a. 1.12 cm
b. 0.90 cm
c. 1.02 cm
d. 3.00 cm
e. None of the above

Answer: 1.02 cm

11. A 500 g mass is dropped from a height of 20 cm above a vertical spring of spring constant 250 N/m. Calculate the displacement of the spring when the mass stops its descent

a. 12 cm
b. 9 cm
c. 11 cm
d. 13 cm
e. None of the above

Answer: 11cm

12. A horizontal spring of spring constant 480 N/m is struck by a 6.0 kg mass moving over a flat surface of coefficient of friction 0.20. If the spring is compressed 12 cm; Calculate the speed of the block when it initially strikes the spring

a. 1.12 m/s
b. 0.90 m/s
c. 1.17 m/s
d. 3.00 m/s
e. None of the above

Answer: 1.17 m/s

13. An iron bolt is used to to connect two iron plates together. The bolt must withstand shear forces up to about 7,500 N. What is the minimum diameter of the bolt, based on the safety factor of 3.0! (Shear sterngth of cast iron is 1.70×10^8 N/m^2.)

a. 1.6 mm
b. 1.3 mm
c. 1.1 cm
d. 2.1 m
e. None of the above

Answer: None of the above

14. A 2.5 kg mass is suspended from a spring extending it 7.9 cm. The spring constant is:

a. 25 kg/s^2
b. 79 kg/s^2
c. 159 kg/s^2
d. 310 kg/s^2
e. None of the above

Answer: 310 kg/s^2

15. A 2.5 kg mass is suspended from a spring extending it 7.9 cm. If the weight is further displaced its frequency of oscillation would be:

    a. 1.8 Hz
    b. 8.2 Hz
    c. 11 Hz
    d. 31 Hz
    e. None of the above

    Answer: 1.8 Hz

16. A mass-spring system with a 250 g mass moves up and down a distance of 20 cm in 0.74 seconds. Its angular frequency is:

    a. 0.74 rad/s
    b. 8.5 rad/s
    c. 13 rad/s
    d. 20 rad/s
    e. None of the above

    Answer: 8.5 rad/s

17. In a pinball machine, if you must compress a spring 10.0 cm in order to shoot a 100.0 g ball with a speed of 3.0 m/s, the spring constant is:

    a. $25.0 \, N \cdot m$
    b. $30.0 \, N \cdot m$
    c. $60.0 \, N \cdot m$
    d. $90.0 \, N \cdot m$
    e. None of the above

    Answer: $90.0 \, N \cdot m$

10.0 - PROBLEMS

18. A spring of spring constant 1.2×10^4 N/m is at the bottom of a 36° inclined plane, as shown.

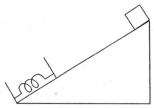

A 25 kg mass is released from rest and compresses the spring 10 cm before stopping. (a) Calculate the speed of the mass as it reaches the spring. (b) Calculate the distance the mass has traveled down the plane, if friction is zero, when the spring is fully compressed.

Answer: (a) 2.0 m/s; (b) 49 cm

19. A graphite fishing pole 1.0 cm in diameter (assumed constant) and 2.0 m long has a 10 N fish on the line (reeled in). If the shear modulus of graphite is 2.5×10^6 N/m^2. Calculate the deflection of the tip of the pole.

Answer: 10 cm

20. Two steel cables 1.0 inches in diameter support a 600 pound elevator cage and a maximum of twelve 160 pound passengers. If Young's Modulus for the steel cable is 250 GPa; (a) Calculate the elongation of the cable at the top floor when it is 16 m long. (b) Calculate the elongation of the cable at the bottom floor when it is 76 m long. (Neglect the weight of the cable itself.)

Answer: (a) 0.71 mm; (b) 3.4 mm

21. A horizontal spring of spring constant 480 N/m is struck by a 6.0 kg mass moving over a flat surface of coefficient of friction 0.20. If the spring is compressed 12 cm; Calculate the distance the mass travels on rebound after compressing the spring.

Answer: 29 cm

22. A horizontal spring of spring constant 1440 N/m is compressed 8.0 cm by a 4.6 kg ball 10 cm in diameter. The ball is released from rest and ejected horizontally on a rough surface by the spring. It then goes up a rough 30° inclined plane. (a) Calculate the speed of the ball as it leaves the spring. (b) Calculate how far up the incline plane the ball goes before stopping.

Answer: (a) 1.2 m/s; (b) 20 cm

23. Two identical, uncompressed, springs of spring constant 320 N/m are connected to a 162 g mass on a

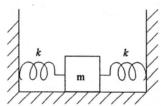

frictionless surface, as shown. If the mass is moved 25 cm to the left and released; calculate the speed of the mass as it passes through the initial equilibrium point.

Answer: 16 m/s

24. Calculate the period of this two spring system using the data of the previous problem and the fact that the effective spring constant is equal to $m\omega^2$ where $\omega = 2\pi/T$ and where T is the time for the mass to make a complete cycle of motion back to its original starting place.

Answer: 100 ms

25. Two identical, uncompressed, springs of spring constant 320 N/m are connected to a 162 g mass on a

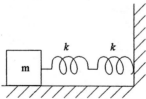

frictionless surface, as shown. If the mass is moved 25 cm to the left and released; Calculate the speed of the mass as it passes through the initial equilibrium point.

Answer: 7.9 m/s

26.   Calculate the period of this two spring system using the data of the previous problem and the fact that the effective spring constant is equal to $m\omega^2$ where $\omega = 2\pi/T$ and where T is the time for the mass to make a complete cycle of motion back to its original starting position.

Answer: 200 ms

27.   A cylinder of 162 g mass is connected at its axis to two identical springs of spring constant 320 N/m, as

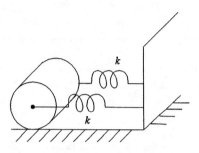

shown. The axis of the cylinder is displaced 25 cm to the left from its equilibrium position and released. The cylinder rolls without slipping. Calculate the speed of the cylinder as it passes through its original equilibrium position.

Answer: 13 m/s

28.   A 5.0 m long uniform beam of 500 kg mass supports a 2750 kg load by means of a steel cable, as

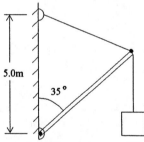

supports a 2750 kg load by means of a steel cable, as shown. The support pin for the beam is 10.0 cm long and can distort 1.0% of its radius before shearing. The shear modulus is 80 GPa. Calculate the minimum diameter of the pin.

Answer: 1.0 cm

29.   A woofer speaker vibrates with an amplitude of 1.8 cm at a frequency of 80 Hz. (a) Calculate the time until the speaker makes its second excursion through the equilibrium position from a maximum displacement. (b) Calculate the speed of the speaker as it passes through equilibrium. (c) Calculate the maximum acceleration.

Answer: (a) 9.4×10^{-3} s; (b) 9.0 m/s; (c) 4.6×10^3 m/s^2

30.   A massless vertical spring of spring constant 49 kg/s^2 has a 360 g mass attached and then is released from its unstretched position. (a) Calculate the distance the mass travels before stopping after release. (b) Calculate the frequency of oscillation. (c) Calculate the maximum speed the mass obtains.

Answer: (a) 14 cm; (b) 1.9 Hz; (c) 0.84 m/s

31.   A fisherman uses a spring scale in his tackle box to weigh his fish. The spring in the scale can compress 16 cm and the maximum weight is marked 25 pounds. (a) Calculate the spring constant (N/m). The markings near the center of the scale are obliterated, but he notes the fish oscillates 8 times in 5 seconds when hung on the scale. (b) Calculate the weight of the fish in pounds.

Answer: (a) 695 N/m; (b) 15.2 lb

32.   A 30 N weight rests against a spring on a frictionless 30° inclined plane, as shown. The spring is

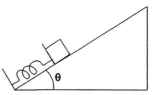

initially compressed 25 cm. (a) Calculate the spring constant. The weight is then displaced 10 cm and released. (b) Calculate the angular frequency of oscillation. (c) Calculate the period of oscillation.

Answer: (a) 60 kg/s^2; (b) 7.0 rad/s; (c) 0.90 s

33.   A child hangs three identical 100 g masses on a spring, as shown, stretching it 10.5 cm.

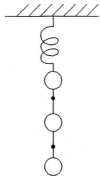

After coming to rest, the bottom mass falls off. (a) Calculate the amplitude of oscillation of the remaining masses. (b) Calculate the frequency of oscillation. (c) Calculate the period of oscillation.

Answer: (a) 7.0 cm; (b) 1.9 Hz; (c) 0.53 s

34.   A 240 g mass, at rest, slides down a 30° frictionless incline plane a distance of 16 cm

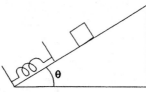

before striking a spring, of spring constant 56 kg/s^2, to which it adheres. (a) Calculate the amount the spring is compressed. (b) Calculate the amplitude of the resulting oscillations. (c) Calculate the frequency of oscillation.

Answer: (a) 8.2 cm; (b) 6.1 cm; (c) 2.4 Hz

CHAPTER 11

11.0 - MULTIPLE CHOICE QUESTIONS

1. A 110 Hz sound wave traveling at a speed of 330 m/s has a wave length of:

    a. 0.33 m
    b. 1.1 m
    c. 3.0 m
    d. 3.3 m
    e. None of the above

    Answer: 3.0 m

2. A wave traveling along a string takes 0.25 seconds to go from its lowest point to its highest point at a particular location along the string. If the wave length is 1.2 m, the speed of the traveling wave is:

    a. 0.83 m/s
    b. 1.0 m/s
    c. 1.2 m/s
    d. 2.4 m/s
    e. None of the above

    Answer: 2.4 m/s

3. The speed of a transverse wave in a 2.5 m long cord of 50 g mass under 288 N tension is:

    a. 29 m/s
    b. 100 m/s
    c. 120 m/s
    d. 1.4×10^4 m/s
    e. None of the above

    Answer: 120 m/s

4. A mol of helium (4.0 g) at STP has a measured speed of sound of 965 m/s. Its bulk modulus is, therefore:

    a. 1.7×10^2 N/m^2
    b. 5.6×10^3 N/m^2
    c. 9.2×10^4 N/m^2
    d. 1.7×10^5 N/m^2
    e. None of the above

    Answer: 1.7×10^5 N/m^2

5. A violin string 32 cm long and 1.8 g mass sounds a 528 Hz note as a fundamental (half wave length up and down motion), the tension in the string is:

    a. 640 N
    b. 270 N
    c. 2.7×10^3 N
    d. 6.4×10^4 N

e.   None of the above

Answer: 640 N

6.   A 50 dB and 60 dB sound levels are mixed to form a sound level of:

a.   50 dB
b.   60 dB
c.   70 dB
d.   110 dB
e.   None of the above

Answer: 60 dB

7.   The fifth harmonic of a guitar string has how many antinodes?

a.   3
b.   4
c.   5
d.   6
e.   None of the above

Answer: 5

8.   A violin string has fundamental frequency of 920 Hz. The string is 20 cm long and weighs 0.75 g. The tension in the string is:

a. 1.2×10^2 N
b. 5.1×10^2 N
c. 6.4×10^2 N
d. 8.2×10^2 N
e.   None of the above

Answer: 5.1×10^2 N

9.   Three tuning forks, each of different frequency, are brought together to produce beat frequencies. The minimum number of such frequencies are:

a.   1
b.   2
c.   3
d.   4
e.   None of the above

Answer: 2

10.   A fire engine is coming toward you at 80 km/h sounding a 1000 Hz siren. If you are traveling toward the fire engine at 80 km/h, you would hear:

a.   879 Hz
b.   1000 Hz
c.   1069 Hz
d.   1138 Hz
e.   None of the above

Answer: 1138 Hz

11. A whistling streamer of frequency 1200 Hz is swung on a string in a 5.0 m diameter horizontal circle at 100 rpm. The highest frequency heard by a bystander would be:

   a. 982 Hz
   b. 1095 Hz
   c. 1200 Hz
   d. 1327 Hz
   e. None of the above

   Answer: None of the above

12. Hydrogen gas is found to emit light of 434 nm wavelength. The "red shift" of a distant galaxy emits light of 458 nm from hydrogen. The speed of the galaxy relative to earth is:

   a. 8.2×10^5 km/h
   b. 4.8×10^6 km/h
   c. 6.0×10^7 km/h
   d. 7.5×10^7 km/h
   e. None of the above

   Answer: 6.0×10^7 km/h

13. A point source radiates 8.0 W of sound power. The intensity at 4.0 m away is:

   a. 0.040 W/m^2
   b. 0.080 W/m^2
   c. 0.25 W/m^2
   d. 0.50 W/m^2
   e. None of the above

   Answer: 0.040 W/m^2

14. A point source radiates 8.0 W of sound power. The sound level, in dB, at 9.0 m is:

   a. 80 dB
   b. 86 dB
   c. 99 dB
   d. 106 dB
   e. None of the above

   Answer: 99 dB

15. At a distance of 30 m the sound of a jet plane has the intensity of 140 dB. Ignoring the refelctions from the ground, what is the intensity at the distance of 300 m?

   a. 80 dB
   b. 86 dB
   c. 99 dB
   d. 120 dB
   e. None of the above

   Answer: 120 dB

16. A 20 cm long string of 0.65 g mass is under 170 N of tension. The ratio of the wavelength of the waves in air to that on the string is:

    a.   0.7
    b.   1.2
    c.   1.5
    d.   2.5
    e.   None of the above

                                                  Answer: 1.5

17. A violin string 32 cm long and 1.8 g mass sounds a 528 Hz note as a fundamental (half wave length up and down motion), by about how much should the string be shortened to sound a 880 Hz note?

    a.   8.8 cm
    b.   13 cm
    c.   19 cm
    d.   26 cm
    e.   None of the above

                                                 Answer: 13 cm

11.0 - PROBLEMS

18. The equation of a transverse wave in a long string can be written $y = A \sin(kx - wt)$, where A is the amplitude, $k = 2\pi/\lambda$, and $w = 2\pi f$. If the amplitude is 2.5 mm and a 100 Hz wave travels at 25 m/s; (a) Calculate the wave vector, k. (b) Calculate the maximum transverse wave speed. (c) Calculate the displacement at $x = 7.5$ cm, $t = 0.25$ s.

                     Answer: (a) 8π m^{-1}; (b) $\pi/2$ m/s; (c) -1.0 mm

19. A 4.8 m long rope weighs 0.8 N and is tied to a wall. The free end is under a tension of 36 N. If a disturbance is introduced at the free end; (a) Calculate the time for it to return after reflection. (b) Calculate the phase difference of the returning wave. If a second identical disturbance is introduced 0.052 s after the first; (c) Calculate the distance from the free end to where the disturbances meet. (d) Calculate the amplitude of the returning wave after they meet.

                     Answer: (a) 0.21 s; (b) 180°; (c) 3.6 m; (d) zero

20. A plucked violin string emits its lowest frequency of 440 Hz (A_4). The string is 28 cm long and has a 190 N tension. (a) Calculate the mass of the string. (b) Calculate the next higher frequency (second harmonic). (c) Calculate the change in length of the string to produce the C_5 note (523.25 Hz).

                     Answer: (a) 0.88 g; (b) 880 Hz; (c) 4.5 cm

21. Two hi-fi speakers, 3.2 m apart, are 4.8 m

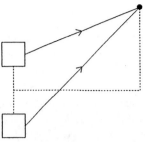

from the end of a room. A person sits 2.5 m above a line from the midpoint between the speakers to the end of the room, as shown. Both speakers emit an in phase 100 Hz tone. (a) Calculate the distance from the person to the nearest speaker. (b) Calculate the distance from the person to the farthest speaker. (c) Calculate the phase difference of sound from speakers as noted by the person.

Answer: (a) 4.9 m; (b) 6.3 m; (c) 150°

22. Often it is possible to hear an approaching train by putting the ear to the track (we strongly recommend against doing this experiment). How long does it take for the wave to travel down the steel track if the train is 1.0 km away? ($\rho_{Steel} = 7.8 \times 10^3$ kg/m^3; $Y = 200 \times 10^9$ N/m^2).

Answer: 0.20 s

23. A 1.5 MHz sound wave travels through 2.6 m of air ($v = 344$ m/s) then through 1.6 cm of aluminum ($v = 6420$ m/s) and then through 1.8 m of helium ($v = 965$ m/s) before arriving at a detector. (a) Calculate the transit time of the wave. (b) Calculate the wavelength of the sound in aluminum. (c) Calculate the wavelength of sound in helium.

Answer: (a) 9.43 ms; (b) 4.28 mm; (c) 0.643 mm

24. A point source radiates 82 dB of sound at a distance of 2.8 m. (a) Calculate the power of the source. (b) Calculate the sound intensity, in dB, at 10 m distance from the source.

Answer: (a) 1.56×10^{-2} W; (b) 71 dB

25. A 60 cm long cord of 75 g mass is fixed at one end. The other end is attached to an electrically driven tuning fork vibrating perpendicularly to the cord at 100 Hz. (a) Calculate the tension in the cord in order to vibrate in three antinodes. (b) Calculate the tension in the cord for two antinodes.

Answer: (a) 200 N; (b) 450 N

26. A stone is dropped into a well and a splash is heard 2.5 s later as the stone strikes the water, then a dull thud 2.8 s later as the stone strikes the bottom. (a) Calculate the depth of the well ($v = 344$ m/s) to the surface of the water. (b) Calculate the depth of the water ($v = 1400$ m/s) if the stone sinks at 10 m/s.

Answer: (a) 28.7 m; (b) 3 m

27. An earthquake generates transverse waves or S waves ($v = 4.5$ kps) and longitudinal or P waves ($v = 8.0$ kps) in the earth's crust. A seismograph records S and P waves from a quake 2 min 48 sec apart. Calculate the distance to the epicenter of the quake from the seismograph.

Answer: 1728 km

28. At 1500 m a 500 Hz siren is barely audible (20 dB). Calculate the distance at which it would be painful to hear (122 dB).

Answer: 1.2 cm

29.   A 10 m high closed oil storage tank is partially filled with oil. The air above the oil has a density of 1.2×10^{-3} g/cm^3 and bulk modulus 1.5×10^5 Pa. Tapping the top of the tank causes a 20 Hz resonance. Calculate the depth of the oil in the tank.

Answer: 1.15 m

30.   A fire engine with a 1000 Hz siren moves away from you at 80 kph toward a large, tall building which reflects sound back to you. (a) Calculate the frequency of the siren that you hear. (b) Calculate the frequency of the reflected sound that you hear. (c) Calculate the frequency of the reflected sound that the fire engine crew hears.

Answer: (a) 939 Hz (b) 1069 Hz (c) 1138 Hz

31.   The sun has a diameter of about 1.4×10^9 m and rotates with a period of 24.7 days. Calculate the maximum Doppler shift of the wavelength of blue light (450 nm) from the edge of the sun.

Answer: 3.1×10^{-3} nm

32.   A 10 cm wavelength radar notes a 1200 Hz beat frequency when the reflected signal from an approach aircraft mixes with the transmitted signal. Calculate the speed of the aircraft.

Answer: 216 km/h

33.   At an airport, departing jets can emit a sound intensity of 150 dB maximum at 100 m above the end of the departure runway. If the jets climb at an angle of 45°, calculate the distance from the end of the runway that houses can be built so as not to exceed 120 dB of noise of the departing jets.

Answer: 4.47 km

34.   A supersonic aircraft generates a conical shockwave whose angle of the cone with respect to the direction of motion is given as $\sin \theta = v/V$, where V is the speed of the aircraft. The shock wave on the ground is called a sonic boom. A plane traveling at Mach 1.5 (1.5 times the speed of sound) passes overhead and the sonic boom is heard 52.6 s later. Calculate the altitude of the aircraft in feet.

Answer: 34,000 ft

CHAPTER 12

12.0 - MULTIPLE CHOICE QUESTIONS

1.   The Fahrenheit and Kelvin scales give the same reading at:

   a.   −655° F
   b.   0 K
   c.   273 K
   d.   575° F
   e.   None of the above

   Answer: 575° F

2.   The temperature at which the Fahrenheit scale reading is twice that of the Celsius scale reading is:

   a.   −320° F
   b.   160° C
   c.   212° C
   d.   320° C
   e.   None of the above

   Answer: 160° C

3.   If the diameter of a hole in a copper plate is 1.00 inches at 20° C, its diameter in boiling water is:

   a.   2.540 cm
   b.   2.541 cm
   c.   2.543 cm
   d.   1.010 in
   e.   None of the above

   Answer: 2.543 cm

4.   A brass sphere with a diameter of 16 cm at 68° F is heated to 284° F. The change in volume of the sphere is:

   a. 6.72×10^{-3} cm^3
   b.   14.4 cm^3
   c.   25.9 cm^3
   d.   115 cm^3
   e.   None of the above

   Answer: 14.4 cm^3

5.   1.0 liters of a gas at STP expands to 1.5 liters and 1.25×10^5 Pa. The final temperature of the gas is:

   a.   233° C
   b.   273° C
   c.   326° C
   d.   507° C
   e.   None of the above

6. An automobile tire of 1200 in^3 volume contains air at a gauge pressure of 28 psi at 68° F. In use, the temperature rises to 96° F and the pressure reads 30 psi. The volume of the tire in use is:

   a. 1180 in^3
   b. 1208 in^3
   c. 1580 in^3
   d. 1990 in^3
   e. None of the above

   Answer: 1208 in^3

7. The number of gas molecules/cm^3 in a vacuum of 10^{-12} atm at 20° C is:

   a. 8.6×10^6
   b. 1.5×10^7
   c. 2.5×10^7
   d. 3.7×10^8
   e. None of the above

   Answer: 2.5×10^7

8. The rms speed of electrons ($m = 9.1 \times 10^{-31}$ kg) in the sun's corona which has a temperature of about 1.5×10^6 K is:

   a. 1.6×10^3 m/s
   b. 3.8×10^4 m/s
   c. 4.2×10^5 m/s
   d. 8.3×10^6 m/s
   e. None of the above

   Answer: 8.3×10^6 m/s

9. The temperature at which helium atoms (6.64×10^{-24} g) reach the rms speed to escape from earth (11.2 km/s) is:

   a. 2.0×10^4 K
   b. 3.8×10^4 K
   c. 4.2×10^5 K
   d. 6.0×10^5 K
   e. None of the above

   Answer: 2.0×10^4 K

10. A cylinder, 10 cm in diameter, confines an ideal gas at 20° C by a massless, movable piston 8 cm from the bottom when a 12 kg weight is on top, as shown. The number of moles of gas confined is:

    a.   0.004
    b.   0.01
    c.   0.03
    d.   0.2
    e.   None of the above

Answer: 0.03

11. A cylinder, 10 cm in diameter, confines an ideal gas at 20° C by a massless, movable piston 8 cm from the bottom when a 12 kg weight is on top, as shown. If the weight is doubled without changing the temperature of the gas, the distance the piston now is from the bottom is:

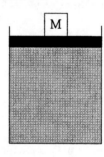

    a.   4.0 cm
    b.   4.8 cm
    c.   6.5 cm
    d.   7.1 cm
    e.   None of the above

Answer: 7.1 cm

12. An aluminum flag pole is 33.0 m long at 68° F. If the temperature drops to −40° F, the length of the flag pole now is:

    a.   32.62 m
    b.   32.78 m
    c.   32.88 m
    d.   32.95 m
    e.   None of the above

Answer: 32.95 m

13. A wooden wagon wheel at 68° F is 44 inches in diameter. At what temperature would the corresponding iron rim be approximately 1/4 inch larger in diameter?

   a. 640° F
   b. 730° F
   c. 890° F
   d. 1850° F
   e. None of the above

   Answer: 640° F

14. The average kinetic energy of a hydrogen gas at STP in a cubical volume 10 cm on an edge is:

   a. 2.74×10^{-22} J
   b. 5.65×10^{-21} J
   c. 165 J
   d. 340 J
   e. None of the above

   Answer: 165 J

15. An iron ring is to fit snugly on a cylindrical iron rod. At 20°C, the diameter of the rod is 6.453 cm and the inside diameter of the ring is 6.420 cm. To what temperature must the ring be heated if its hole is to be large enough so it will slip over the rod? ($\alpha = 12 \times 10^{-6} C^{-1}$.)

   a. $1,200^0$ C
   b. 430^0 C
   c. 100^0 C
   d. 512^0 C
   e. None of the above

   Answer: 430^0 C

16. Blocks of concrete 10 m long are placed end to end with no space between them to allow for expansion. If the blocks were placed at a temperature of 10^0C, what will be the force of compressions when the temperature reaches 40^0C? The contact area between each block is 0.20 m^2. ($\alpha = 12 \times 10^{-6} C^{-1}$.)

   a. 2.74×10^6 N/m^2
   b. 7.0×10^6 N/m^2
   c. 3.45×10^8 N/m^2
   d. 9.8×10^8 N/m^2
   e. None of the above

   Answer: 7.0×10^6 N/m^2

17. Assume that there is roughly 4.5 billion people in the world. The ratio of the number of molecules (SiO_2) in a grain of sand (cube 0.1 mm on an edge and density 2.3 g/cm^3) to the number of people in the world is about:

   a. 2×10^3
   b. 5×10^6
   c. 2×10^8
   d. 5×10^9

e. None of the above

Answer: 5×10^6

12.0 - PROBLEMS

18. A stainless steel wire ($Y = 190$ GPa) of 0.80 mm diameter is heated to 1000° C and then attached tautly between two rigid supports. Calculate the tension in the wire as it cools to 68° F.

Answer: 1.62×10^3 N

19. On a cold day (32° F) you fill your tank to the top with 18 gallons of gas (at 32° F) at the station next to your house. You then park in your heated (68° F) garage. (a) Calculate the number of gallons of gas that overflows from your tank. You next park your car outside and the temperature drops to −40° F. (b) Calculate the number of gallons of gas in your tank.

Answer: (a) 0.342; (b) 16.65

20. Calculate the change in area of a copper plate 20 cm × 15 cm as the temperature rises from 68° F to 428° F.

Answer: 1.99 cm^2

21. The brass pendulum of a clock is set to keep accurate time at 20° C with a 2 second period. (a) Find the change in the period at 36° C. (b) Calculate the error in the time after 30 days.

Answer: (a) 3.024×10^{-4} s; (b) 6 min 32 s, slow

22. A 1 inch cube of Lucite ($\rho = 1.182$ g/cm^3, $\beta = 2.7 \times 10^{-5}$/K) floats in a beaker of glycerin ($\rho = 1.261$ g/ml, $\beta = 5.05 \times 10^{-4}$/K) at 20° C. Calculate the temperature at which the Lucite starts to sink.

Answer: 160° C

23. A 25 liter cylinder contains oxygen at 15 atm gauge pressure at 20° C. The cylinder is heated to 80° C; however, it is determined by weighing that 36 g of gas escaped due to a leaky valve. (a) Calculate the number of moles originally in the cylinder. (b) Calculate the final gauge pressure in atm.

Answer: (a) 16.6 moles; (b) 17 atm

24. A 60 liter gas cylinder contains CO at a gauge pressure of 100 psi at 68° F. The tank is then filled with 20 moles more of CO causing the temperature to rise to 86° F. (a) Calculate the mass of gas originally in the cylinder. (b) Calculate the final gauge pressure in psi.

Answer: (a) 544 g; (b) 226 psi

25. A container has 10 liters of Argon at STP. (a) Calculate the number of particles of gas in the container. (b) Calculate the rms speed of the particles.

Answer: (a) 2.69×10^{23}; (b) 413 m/s

26. Consider the numbers 3, 5, 7, 11, 13, and 17. (a) Calculate the average of these numbers. (b) Calculate the rms value of these numbers. (c) Calculate the ratio of the rms value to the average value. (d) Replace 17 by 27 and calculate the ratio of the rms value to the average value for this case.

Answer: (a) 9.33; (b) 10.5; (c) 1.124; (d) 1.232

27. A helium tank holds 10 cu ft of He at 120 psi absolute at 68° F. The tank is connected to a weather balloon which it inflates until the pressure drops to 75 psi absolute. (a) Calculate the volume of the inflated weather balloon in cu ft (neglect elastic forces of the balloon). (b) Calculate the net buoyancy force lifting the balloon (density of air 1.21 kg/m^3 at 20° C).

Answer: (a) 30.6; (b) 8.87 N

28. A tank contains 1 g of hydrogen gas and an identical tank contains 1 g of oxygen gas at the same temperature. (a) Calculate the ratio of the pressure of hydrogen gas to oxygen. (b) Calculate the ratio of the rms speed of hydrogen gas to oxygen.

Answer: (a) 16; (b) 1

29. A copper penny is taken from ice water and dropped into boiling water. (a) Calculate the percent increase in diameter. (b) Calculate the percent increase in face area. (c) Calculate the percent increase in volume.

Answer: (a) 0.166%; (b) 0.332%; (c) 0.56%

30. The Bulova Accutron watch employs a small tuning fork in place of the pendulum to measure time in a manner identical to the pendulum. The frequency of the fork varies with length the same as it does for the pendulum clock. If the quartz tuning fork is exact at 77° F. (a) Calculate the percent error in frequency at −40° F.   (b) Calculate the percent error in frequency at 122° F.

Answer: (a) 1.79×10^{-3}%; (b) 6.88×10^{-4}%

31. An aluminum strip 1.00 cm long at 20° C is to be laid upon a copper strip in a delicate instrument. Calculate the length of the copper strip so that there is no difference in length of these two strips at 100° C.

Answer: 1.001 cm

32. A flexible container of oxygen (O_2 molecular mass is 32 u; u $= 1.66 \times 10^{-27}$kg) at STP has volume of 10.0 m^3. What is the mass of gas enclosed?

Answer: 14.3 kg

33. An automobile tire is filled to a gauge pressure of 200 kPa at 10^{0}C. After driving 100 km, the temperature within the tire rises to 40^{0}C. What is the pressure within the tire now?

Answer: 333 kPa.

34. An aluminum beaker of 6.0 cm ID and 5.0 cm IH is filled to the top with mercury at 20° C. The temperature of the beaker and mercury is raised to 120° C. (a) Calculate the change in volume of the beaker. (b) Calculate the amount of mercury in ml that spills out (neglect surface tension of mercury).

Answer: (a) 1.02 cm^3; (b) 1.56 ml

CHAPTER 13

13.0 - MULTIPLE CHOICE QUESTIONS

1.   A BTU is the amount of energy required to raise 1 lb of water 1° F. A BTU corresponds to:

    a.   72 cal
    b.   252 cal
    c.   454 cal
    d.   815 cal
    e.   None of the above

                                                    Answer: 252 cal

2.   The heat energy required to increase the temperature of 120 g of copper from 20° C to 180° C is:

    a. 1.8×10^3 J
    b. 1.8×10^4 J
    c. 7.5×10^3 J
    d. 4.2×10^4 J
    e.   None of the above

                                                    Answer: 7.5×10^3 J

3.   A jelly donut has 225 cal. This amount of energy is equivalent to burning a 100 W light bulb for:

    a.   2.6 hours
    b.   3.7 hours
    c.   4.2 hours
    d.   5.2 hours
    e.   None of the above

                                                    Answer: 2.6 hours

4.   150 ml of water at 30° C is mixed with 25 ml of ethyl alcohol at 0° C. The final temperature of the mixture is:

    a.   20° C
    b.   26° C
    c.   290 K
    d.   72° F
    e.   None of the above

                                                    Answer: 72° F

5.   100 g of ice at 0° C is dropped into 500 ml of boiling water. The final temperature of the mixture at equilibrium is:

    a.   28° C
    b.   70° C
    c.   86° C
    d.   92° C

e.   None of the above

Answer: 70° C

6.   The increase in temperature of a liter of water at 20° C due to the complete combustion of 7.6 g of denatured alcohol is:

    a.   29° C
    b.   36° C
    c.   49° C
    d.   69° C
    e.   None of the above

Answer: 49° C

7.   The molar specific heat of carbon monoxide in cal/mol · K is:

    a.   0.25
    b.   7.0
    c.   11
    d.   28
    e.   None of the above

Answer: 7.0

8.   A copper radiator 2.0 mm thick and area 90 cm^2 has water inside at 80° C and air outside keeping the surface at 20° C. The rate of heat transfer is:

    a. 1.0×10^5 W
    b. 5.0×10^5 W
    c. 1.0×10^6 W
    d. 5.0×10^6 W
    e.   None of the above

Answer: 1.0×10^5 W

9.   A traveler immerses a 180 W electric heater into a paper cup of 8 oz. of water at 68° F. The time to bring the water to a boil is:

    a.   3.0 minutes
    b.   4.2 minutes
    c.   5.6 minutes
    d.   7.0 minutes
    e.   None of the above

Answer: 7.0 minutes

10.   A 200 g lead pellet at 72° F falls 1.8 m in 50 ml of water at 72° F. The maximum temperature rise possible is:

    a. 3.0×10^{-2} °F
    b. 4.5×10^{-2} °F
    c. 4.5×10^{-2} °C
    d. 8.0×10^{-2} °C
    e.   None of the above

11. 10 g of ice at 0° C and 50 ml of water at boiling temperature are mixed with 50 ml of water at 25° C. The final temperature of the mixture is:

   a. 28° C
   b. 42° C
   c. 50° C
   d. 62° C
   e. None of the above

   Answer: 50° C

12. The thermal conductivity of Pyrex glass is 1.2×10^{-2} W/cm · K. The corresponding value in BTU/hr. · ft ° F is:

   a. 0.69
   b. 8.4
   c. 16
   d. 120
   e. None of the above

   Answer: 0.69

13. A 100 ml of water at 158° F cools to 72° F uniformly in $3\frac{1}{3}$ minutes. The heat energy flow rate must be:

   a. 35 J/s
   b. 58 J/s
   c. 72 J/s
   d. 100 J/s
   e. None of the above

   Answer: 100 J/s

14. A 250 g aluminum slug at LN temperature (77 K) is dropped into 150 ml of water at 100° C. The final temperature at equilibrium is:

   a. −108° C
   b. −77° C
   c. 22° C
   d. 36° C
   e. None of the above

   Answer: 22° C

15. If 200 cm^3 of tea at 95°C is poured into a 150 g glass cup initially at 25°C, what will be the final temperature of the mixture when equilibrium is reached, assuming that no heat flows into the surroundings? (assume that tea is essentially water - $c = 4,180$ J/kg C; $c_{glass}=840$ J/kg C)

   a. 89° C
   b. 77° C
   c. 56° C
   d. 90° C

87

e.   None of the above

16. How much heat does the refrigerator has to remove from a 1.5 kg of water at 20^0C to make ice at -12^0C?

($c_{H_2O} = 4,180$ J/kg C; $c_{ice} = 2,100$ J/kg C)

a.   700 kJ
b.   1.000 kJ
c.   660 kJ
d.   512 kJ
e.   None of the above

Answer: 660 kJ

17. Heat flows from the hot earth's core to the surface at the rate of about 0.060 W/m². Assuming the average thermal conductivity of the earth's mantle is 2.0 W/m K, the depth one must drill from a 68° F surface to reach the boiling point of water is:

a.   1.5 km
b.   2.7 km
c.   4.2 km
d.   12.6 km
e.   None of the above

Answer: 2.7 km

13.0 - PROBLEMS

18. A glass beaker of 100 g mass is at 22° C. It is filled with 50 ml of water at 36° C. Calculate the final equilibrium temperature.

Answer: 32° C

19. The mass equivalent of a calorimeter is the mass of water that has the same heat absorption as the actual calorimeter. A 100 ml of water at 80° C is poured into a calorimeter at 25° C. The final equilibrium temperature is 75° C. Calculate the mass equivalent of this calorimeter.

Answer: 10 g

20. The mass equivalent of a calorimeter is the mass of water that has the same heat absorption as the actual calorimeter. A 100 ml of water at 80° C is poured into a calorimeter at 25° C. The final equilibrium temperature is 75° C. Calculate the specific heat of a 170 g metal sample that is removed from boiling water and placed into this calorimeter containing 100 ml of water at 20° C if the final equilibrium tempera-ture is 30° C.

Answer: 0.092 cal/g K

21. Calculate the heat energy required to increase the temperature of a 100 g, 25 liter stainless steel cylinder of xenon gas at 10 atm from 20° C to 180° C.

Answer: 1.29×10^4 cal

22. Calculate the mass of propane that must be completely burned to heat 1.0 gals of water from 68° F to steam at 212° F.

Answer: 741 g

23. A circular rod of 0.10 cm diameter and 2.0 cm long is constructed by joining a 1.75 cm silver rod to a 0.25 cm brass rod. The free end of the brass rod is at LN temperature, 77 K; whereas, the free end of the silver rod is at 20° C. Calculate the temperature at the interface of these two metals.

Answer: 165 K

24. A circular rod of 0.10 cm diameter and 2.0 cm long is constructed by joining a 1.75 cm silver rod to a 0.25 cm brass rod. The free end of the brass rod is at LN temperature, 77 K; whereas, the free end of the silver rod is at 20° C. Calculate the number of moles of nitrogen evaporated each hour by this rod.

Answer: 1.51 moles

25. Two identical metal strips of iron and lead are fused on top of one another to form a bar 1.0 cm × 8.0 cm × 0.20 mm thick. If one end of the bar is at 0° C and the other at 100° C. Calculate the heat flow rate of the composite bar.

Answer: 135 mJ/s

26. A 150 g aluminum cylinder, open at the top, has a 10 cm ID and is filled to a depth of 4.0 cm with water at 20° C. Calculate the amount of heat that must be removed to form ice on top of 3.5 cm of water.

Answer: 1.0×10^4 cal

27. A 150 g aluminum cylinder, open at the top, has a 10 cm ID and is filled to a depth of 4.0 cm with water at 20° C. Calculate the time required to form ice on top of 3.5 cm of water if the cylinder is in a 100 W (heat removal rate) refrigerator.

Answer: 7.0 min

28. You decide to lose 1.0 lbs of fat by weightlifting a 200 lb weight 30 inches. Calculate the number of repetitions required to burn this pound of fat.

Answer: 25,420 times

29. Calculate the number of moles of propane ($CH_3 CH_2 CH_3$) that must be burned at 25% efficiency in heating of 50 ml of water at 20° C into steam in a 150 g glass beaker.

Answer: 2.54×10^{-2} moles

30. Two copper rods; one of length

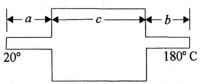

$a = 5.0$ cm and diameter 2.0 mm, the other of length $b = 8.0$ cm and diameter 1.0 mm; are joined to a brass rod of length $c = 2.5$ cm and diameter 1.0 cm, as shown. The first rod has its free end at 20° C, the other copper rod has its free end at 180° C. Calculate the heat energy flow rate.

Answer: 0.518 J/s

31. A 75 g glass thermometer at 10° C is inserted into a 10 g mass equivalent calorimeter containing water at 25° C. The final temperature registered on the thermometer is 22° C. Calculate the quantity of water in the calorimeter.

Answer: 50 ml

32. A major source of heat loss from a house is through the windows. Claculate the rate of heat flow through a glass window 2.0 m × 1.5 m in area and 3.2 mm thick of the temperature at the inner and outer surfaces are 15.0^0C and 14.0^0C, respectively. (thermal conductivity of typical glass is 0.84 J/s m C.)

Answer: 790 W

33. What is the rate of energy absorption from the sun by a person lying flat on the beach on a clear day if the sun makes a 30^0 angle with the vertical? Assume that the emissivity $e = 0.70$, the area of the body exposed to the sun is 0.80 m^2, and that 1,000 W/m^2 reaches the earth's surface.

Answer: 490 W

34. 5 liters of steam at 1.0 atm pressure and 212° F is vented into a perfect (massless) calorimeter at $-10°$ C containing 100 g of ice at this temperature. Calculate the amount of water (liquid) produced.

Answer: 28.2 ml

CHAPTER 14

14.0 - MULTIPLE CHOICE QUESTIONS

1. The work done in compressing 1.0 liters of gas, isochorically, from 1.0 atm to 5.0 atm is:

   a. −4.0 J
   b. 0 J
   c. 4.0 J
   d. 8.0 J
   e. None of the above

   Answer: 0 J

2. The work done in compressing 0.25 moles of gas, isothermally, from 2.5 liters to 0.5 liters at 100° C is:

   a. -1.25×10^3 J
   b. -3.35×10^2 J
   c. 4.2 J
   d. 2.5×10^2 J
   e. None of the above

   Answer: -1.25×10^3 J

3. The work done in going from point A to point B by path a in the figure shown is:

   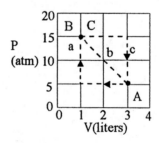

   a. -1.0×10^2 J
   b. -2.0×10^2 J
   c. -1.0×10^3 J
   d. -2.0×10^3 J
   e. None of the above

   Answer: -1.0×10^3 J

4. The work done in going from point A to point B by path b in the figure shown is:

91

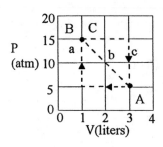

a. -1.0×10^2 J
b. -2.0×10^2 J
c. -1.0×10^3 J
d. -2.0×10^3 J
e. None of the above

Answer: -2.0×10^3 J

5. The work done in going from point A to point B by path a and back to point A by path b in the figure shown is:

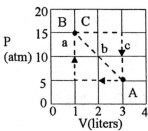

a. -1.0×10^3 J
b. -2.0×10^3 J
c. 1.0×10^3 J
d. 2.0×10^3 J
e. None of the above

Answer: -1.0×10^3 J

6. The work done in going from point A to point B by path a and back to point A by path c in the figure shown above is:

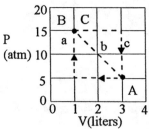

a. -1.0×10^3 J
b. -2.0×10^3 J
c. -3.0×10^3 J
d. 3.0×10^3 J

92

e.   None of the above

Answer: -2.0×10^3 J

7.   The gas in a heat engine goes through the cycle shown providing 100 J of work per cycle. If -8.0 cal of heat is added during process A to B, the amount added during the process B to C is:

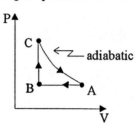

a.   16 cal
b.   32 cal
c.   96 cal
d.   108 cal
e.   None of the above

Answer: 32 cal

8.   The difference in internal energy at C and A is:

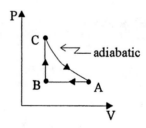

a.   0
b.   8.0 cal
c.   24 cal
d.   96 cal
e.   None of the above

Answer: 24 cal

9.   A Carnot engine operates between ice water and boiling water. Its efficiency is:

a.   22%
b.   25%
c.   27%
d.   100%
e.   None of the above

Answer: 27%

10.   An engine burns gasoline releasing 2.85×10^4 cal/s of heat energy. If the engine's efficiency is 20%, its horsepower output is:

a. 12
b. 20
c. 28
d. 32
e. None of the above

Answer: 32

11. A refrigerator runs on a $\frac{1}{10}$ horsepower motor (100% efficiency) and removes 5 cal/s of heat. Its coefficient of performance is:

a. 7%
b. 16%
c. 20%
d. 28%
e. None of the above

Answer: 28%

12. The change in entropy of 10 ml of water as it melts is:

a. 12 J/K
b. 18 J/K
c. 33 J/K
d. 330 J/K
e. None of the above

Answer: 12 J/K

13. 1.5 moles of a monatomic gas in a container is heated isobarically from 22° C to 215° C. The increase in internal energy is:

a. 1.2×10^3 J
b. 3.6×10^3 J
c. 6.0×10^3 J
d. 7.2×10^3 J
e. None of the above

Answer: 6.0×10^3 J

14. 2.5 moles of an ideal gas expands isothermally at 100° C from 2.5 l to 8.0 l. The work done by the gas is:

a. 8.4×10^2 J
b. 1.2×10^3 J
c. 2.4×10^3 J
d. 9.0×10^3 J
e. None of the above

Answer: 9.0×10^3 J

15. How much energy is transformed in 24 hours by a 65 kg person who spends 8.0 h sleeping, 1.0 h at moderate physical labor, 4.0 h in light activity, and 11.0 h working at a desk or relaxing? (You may assume the following metabolic rates: sleeping 70 W; sitting upright 115 W; light activity 230 W; moderate work 460 W;)

a. 1.15×10^7 J
b. 3.0×10^3 J
c. 0.5×10^7 J
d. 9.0×10^7 J
e. None of the above

Answer: 1.15×10^7 J

16. An ideal gas is slowly compressed at constant pressure of 2.0 atm from 10.0 l to 2.0 l. (In this process some heat flows out and the temperature drops.) Heat is then added to the gas, holding the volume constant, and the pressure and temperature are allowed to rise until the temperature reaches the original value. What is the total work done by the gas?

a. -8.4×10^2 J
b. -1.2×10^3 J
c. -1.6×10^3 J
d. -9.0×10^3 J
e. None of the above

Answer: -1.6×10^3 J

17. An ideal polyatomic gas (e.g., NH_4) has a molar specific heat at constant volume of 24.9 J/mol · K. The corresponding molar specific heat at constant pressure is:

a. 16.6
b. 33.2
c. 42.1
d. 56.0
e. None of the above

Answer: 33.2

14.0 - PROBLEMS

18. 100 g of water at the boiling point is converted to steam at 1.0 atm pressure. (a) Calculate the work done (assume ideal gas). (b) Calculate the energy required. (c) Calculate the change in internal energy involved.

Answer: (a) 1.72×10^4 J; (b) 5.40×10^4 cal; (c) 4.97×10^4 cal

19. 2.5 moles of an ideal diatomic gas in a 2.0 l volume at 10 atm is expanded adiabatically ($\gamma = 1.4$) to 1.0 atm. (a) Calculate the initial temperature of the gas. (b) Calculate the final volume of the gas. (c) Calculate the final temperature of the gas.

Answer: (a) 97.2 K; (b) 10.4 l; (c) 50.3 K

20.　The thermodynamic cycle of 1.5 moles

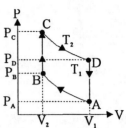

of an ideal diatomic gas, as shown, is comprised of two isothermal processes, A to B at 100° C and C to D at 800° C, and two isochoric processes, B to C at 2.0 L and D to A at 10.0 l. Calculate the pressures P_A, P_B, P_C, and P_D.

Answer:　(a) 4.61 atm;　(b) 23.0 atm;　(c) 66.2 atm;　(d) 13.2 atm

21.　The thermodynamic cycle of 1.5 moles

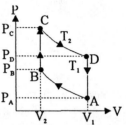

of an ideal diatomic gas, as shown, is comprised of two isothermal processes, A to B at 100° C and C to D at 800° C, and two isochoric processes, B to C at 2.0 L and D to A at 10.0 l. (a) Calculate the work available from this process per cycle. (b) Calculate the horsepower rating of a four-cycle engine operating on this thermodynamic cycle at 4500 rpm.

Answer:　(a) 1.40×10^4 J/cycle;　(b) 706 hp

22.　The thermodynamic cycle of 1.5 moles

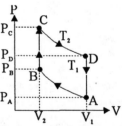

of an ideal diatomic gas, as shown, is comprised of two isothermal processes, A to B at 100° C and C to D at 800° C, and two isochoric processes, B to C at 2.0 L and D to A at 10.0 L. (a) Calculate the internal energy during the process A to B. (b) Calculate the internal energy during the process C to D.

Answer:　(a) 1.16×10^4 J;　(b) 3.35×10^4 J

23. The thermodynamic cycle of 1.5 moles

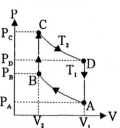

of an ideal diatomic gas, as shown, is comprised of two isothermal processes, A to B at 100° C and C to D at 800° C, and two isochoric processes, B to C at 2.0 l and D to A at 10.0 l. (a) Calculate the efficiency of an engine operating on this cycle. (b) Calculate the corresponding Carnot efficiency.

Answer: (a) 39%; (b) 65%

24. A small two-cycle engine burns 10 mg of gasoline per thermdynamic cycle and delivers 10 horsepower at 3600 rpm. (a) Calculate the heat energy input rate at 3600 rpm. (b) Calculate the efficiency of this engine at 3600 rpm.

Answer: (a) 6.88×10^3 cal/s; (b) 26%

25. Refrigerators are rated in "tons" which is the heat removal rate to freeze 1 ton of water at 32° F to ice at 32° F per day. (a) Calculate the rating in tons of a 100 BTU/hour refrigerator. (b) Calculate the minimum horsepower required for a 10 ton refrigeration unit.

Answer: (a) 0.50 tons; (b) 47 h.p.

26. 2.6 cubic feet of air at 30 psig (gauge pressure) is allowed to expand isothermally to 1.0 atm. It is then cooled isobarically back to 2.6 cubic foot volume. Calculate the work available per thermodynamic cycle.

Answer: 9.97×10^3 J

27. 3.0 g of hydrogen and 24 g of oxygen are confined at 80 psig (gauge pressure). (a) Calculate the pressure contribution of the hydrogen gas. (b) Calculate the pressure contribution of the oxygen gas.

Answer: (a) 4.30 atm; (b) 2.15 atm

28. 0.50 moles of an ideal monatomic gas in a

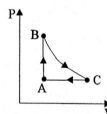

12 l volume at 20° C is heated isochorically to 455° C, A to B, and then expanded isothermally, B to C, and finally compressed isobarically, C to A, as shown. (a) Calculate the work available per cycle. (b) Calculate the heat input per cycle. (c) Calculate the efficiency of this cycle. (d) Calculate the Carnot efficiency.

Answer: (a) 955 J/cycle; (b) 877 cal/cycle; (c) 26%; (d) 60%

29. An ice making machine is powered by a $\frac{1}{3}$ horse power motor and operates at 75% of the Carnot coefficient of performance. The freezing compartment is at 5° F and the outside air temperature is 68° F.

(a) Calculate the coefficient of performance of the ice maker. (b) Calculate the pounds of ice per hour this machine can make.

Answer: (a) 5.53; (b) 30 lb/hr

30. 0.25 moles of an ideal monatomic gas

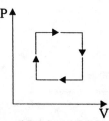

operates on the cycle shown between 1.5 atm and 3.0 atm pressure and 2.0 l and 8.0 l of volume. (a) Calculate the heat input per cycle. (b) Calculate the work available per cycle. (c) Calculate the efficiency of this cycle. (d) Calculate the Carnot efficiency of this cycle.

Answer: (a) 1.19×10^3 cal/cycle; (b) 9.09×10^2 J/cycle; (c) 18.2%; (d) 87.5%

31. 2.5 moles of an ideal diatomic gas undergoes a reversible isothermal expansion at 177° C from 2.0 l to 15 l. (a) Calculate the internal energy of the gas and its change during the expansion. (b) Calculate the heat input required for this expansion. (c) Calculate the entropy change of the gas for this expansion.

Answer: (a) 2.34×10^4 J; (b) 4.50×10^3 J; (c) 41.9 J/K

32. A sample of 50.0 kg of water at 20.0^0C is mixed with 50.0 kg of water at 24.0^0C. What is the change in entropy? (c = 1.00 kcal/kg K)

Answer: +0.002 kcal/K

33. A steam engine operates between 500^0C and 270^0C. What is the maximum possible efficiency of this engine?

Answer: 0.30

34. 150 ml of water at 32° F is mixed with 25 g of ice. Heat is removed in a reversible process until equal amounts of ice and water are present in the mixture. (a) Calculate the amount of heat removed. (b) Calculate the change in entropy of the system. Next, heat is added in a reversible process until only 25 g of ice remains. (c) Calculate the change in entropy of the system for this case.

Answer: (a) 4.98×10^3 cal; (b) -76.4 J/K; (c) 76.4 J/K

CHAPTER 15

15.0 - MULTIPLE CHOICE QUESTIONS

1. Two charges of $+1.0\mu$ C and -2.5μ C experience a force of attraction of 1.0 N; therefore, their separation is:

    a. 5 cm
    b. 10 cm
    c. 15 cm
    d. 20 cm
    e. None of the above

    Answer: 15 cm

2. Three charges of $+1.0\mu$ C, -2.0μ C, and $+3.0\mu$ C are in a line 10 cm apart. The magnitude of the force on the center charge is:

    a. 1.2 N
    b. 1.8 N
    c. 2.4 N
    d. 3.6 N
    e. None of the above

    Answer: 3.6 N

3. Three charges of -2.0μ C, $+1.0\mu$ C, and $+3.0\mu$ C are in a line 12 cm apart. The $+3.0\mu$ C charge is moved relative to the $+1.0\mu$ C charge until the force acting on it is zero. The final distance from the 1.0μ C charge is:

    a. 24 cm
    b. 29 cm
    c. 34 cm
    d. 41 cm
    e. None of the above

    Answer: 29 cm

4. Which of the following represents the number of electrons in 1.12 l of helium gas at STP.

    a. 6×10^{21}
    b. 3×10^{22}
    c. 6×10^{22}
    d. 6×10^{23}
    e. None of the above

    Answer: 6×10^{22}

5. Two charges of $+1.0\mu$ C and -1.0μ C are 1.2 cm apart. The magnitude of the electric field midway between these charges is:

    a. 0

b. 5×10^6 N/C
c. 6×10^6 N/C
d. 1×10^7 N/C
e. None of the above

Answer: 5×10^6 N/C

6. Two charges of $+1.0\mu$ C are 1.2 cm apart. The magnitude of the electric field midway between these charges is:

a. 0
b. 5×10^6 N/C
c. 6×10^6 N/C
d. 1×10^7 N/C
e. None of the above

Answer: 0

7. Two charges, $Q_1 = -2.0\mu$ C and $Q_2 = +8.0\mu$ C are placed, as shown, on a 30° - 60 ° right triangle of sides 1.0 cm and $\sqrt{3}$ cm. The magnitude of the electric field at the field point, F.P., is:

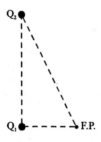

a. 1.8×10^6 N/C
b. 3.6×10^6 N/C
c. 7.2×10^7 N/C
d. 1.8×10^8 N/C
e. None of the above

Answer: 1.8×10^8 N/C

8. Two charges, $Q_1 = -2.0\mu$ C and $Q_2 = +8.0\mu$ C are placed, as shown, on a 30° - 60 ° right triangle of sides 1.0 cm and $\sqrt{3}$ cm. The direction of the electric field at the F.P. relative to a Cartesian coordinate system is:

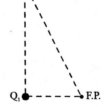

a. 120°
b. 180°
c. 240°

d. 300°
e. None of the above

9. The speed an electron ($m = 9.1 \times 10^{-31}$ kg) at rest attains after 1.0 ns in a 5.7×10^4 N/C electric field is:

a. 1.0×10^7 m/s
b. 2.2×10^7 m/s
c. 3.7×10^7 m/s
d. 4.0×10^7 m/s
e. None of the above

Answer: 1.0×10^7 m/s

10. An 8.0μ C charge is in the center of a cube. The electric flux passing through one face of the cube is:

a. 6.0×10^4 Nm^2/C
b. 1.5×10^5 Nm^2/C
c. 4.5×10^5 Nm^2/C
d. 9.0×10^5 Nm^2/C
e. None of the above

Answer: 1.5×10^5 Nm^2/C

11. A loop antenna of 20 cm diameter is oriented at 45° to a 360 N/C electric field. The electric flux passing through the loop is:

a. 8.0 Nm^2/C
b. 9.4 Nm^2/C
c. 10.2 Nm^2/C
d. 11 Nm^2/C
e. None of the above

Answer: 8.0 Nm^2/C

12. A 3.6 mm diameter plastic rod, 1.2 m long, has 2.4μ C of charge uniformly spread over its surface. The electric field very close to the surface at the middle of the rod is:

a. 2×10^6 N/C
b. 8×10^6 N/C
c. 1×10^7 N/C
d. 2×10^7 N/C
e. None of the above

Answer: 2×10^7 N/C

13. A 5.0 cm diameter conducting sphere has an electric field radially outward. The electric field 5.0 cm from the surface is 100 N/C; therefore, the surface charge density on the sphere is:

a. 2.2×10^{-10} C/m^2
b. 3.5×10^{-9} C/m^2
c. 8.0×10^{-9} C/m^2
d. 1.5×10^{-8} C/m^2

e.   None of the above

Answer: 8.0×10^{-9} C/m^2

14.   A 1.7μ C charge is placed at the corner of a cube. The electric flux passing through the adjacent faces (ones with an edge through the charge) is:

    a.   0
    b. 4×10^2 Nm^2/C
    c. 8×10^3 Nm^2/C
    d. 5×10^4 Nm^2/C
    e.   None of the above

Answer: 0

15.   A 1.7μ C charge is placed at the corner of a cube. The electric flux passing through the opposite faces (not having an edge through the charge) is:

    a.   0
    b. 4×10^2 Nm^2/C
    c. 8×10^3 Nm^2/C
    d. 5×10^4 Nm^2/C
    e.   None of the above

Answer: 8×10^3 Nm^2/C

16.   What is the magnitude of the electric field at a point which is 30cm away from a point charge
       $Q = -3.0 \times 10^{-6}$C?

    a. 4.0×10^5 N/C
    b. 4.0×10^7 N/C
    c. 3.0×10^5 N/C
    d. 3.2×10^7 N/C
    e.   None of the above

Answer: 3.0×10^5 N/C

17.   How far apart must two electrons be if the force between them is to be 2.0×10^{-12} N?

    a. 1.1×10^{-8} m
    b. 1.1×10^8 m
    c. 8×10^{-3} m
    d. 5×10^{-7} m
    e.   None of the above

Answer: 1.1×10^{-8} m

15.0 - PROBLEMS

18.   Two opposite sign charges of 1.6μ C and 2.2μ C are 10 cm apart, separated by an uncompressed spring of spring constant 2.0×10^3 N/m. (a) Calculate the initial force of attraction. (b) Calculate the final separation of the charges as the spring compresses.

Answer: (a) 3.17 N; (b) 2.5 cm

19. An electroscope of sorts is made from two very small 10 g conducting pith balls with $+10\mu$ C of charge on each, with 10 cm long threads suspending them. (a) Calculate the distance between the pith balls ($\tan\theta \simeq \sin\theta$). (b) Calculate the apex angle of the suspending threads.

Answer: (a) 1.23 cm; (b) 7.0°

20. A 10 cm diameter conducting sphere is negatively charged so that an electric field of 10^3 N/C is observed 1.5 m away. (a) Calculate the charge density on the sphere. (b) Calculate the number of moles of electrons required to charge the sphere.

Answer: (a) 8.0×10^{-6} C/m^2; (b) 2.6×10^{-12} moles

21. A proton is placed at each apex of an equilateral triangle of side length 5.2 mm. (a) Calculate the electric field in the center of the triangle. (b) Calculate the magnitude of the electric field at the midpoints of the sides.

Answer: (a) 0; (b) 1.78×10^{-5} N/C

22. An electron ($m = 9.1 \times 10^{-31}$ kg) is accelerated

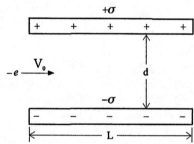

to a speed, v_0, and then injected midway between two metal plates of length L and separation d with a surface charge density $+\sigma$ and $-\sigma$, as shown. (a) Derive an equation for the vertical deflection of the electron as a function of the parameters of the problem. (b) If $L = 10$ cm, $d = 1.0$ cm, and $\sigma = 0.125$ μC/m^2, calculate the speed of the electron in order to just clear the top plate as it exits.

Answer: (a) $y = e\sigma L^2/2m\epsilon_0 v_0^2$; (b) 5.0×10^7 m/s

23. A negative charge of mass m is placed between two metal plates (as in the previous problem) with zero velocity and suspended against gravity by the electric field between the plates. (a) Derive an equation for the surface charge required on each plate in terms of the parameters of the problem. (b) Calculate the charge density necessary to suspend an electron.

Answer: (a) $\sigma = mg\epsilon_0/q$; (b) 4.94×10^{-22} C/m^2

24. In the Bohr model of the hydrogen atom, an electron orbits about a fixed proton like a satellite at a distance of 0.0529 nm. (a) Calculate the speed of the electron in orbit. (b) Calculate the "wavelength" of the electron if this first orbit has only one wavelength around the orbit. (c) Calculate Planck's constant (the product of wavelength and momentum).

Answer: (a) 2.2×10^6 m/s; (b) 3.32×10^{-10} m; (c) 6.62×10^{-34} J$\cdot$S

25. A large flat non-conducting sheet with a positive

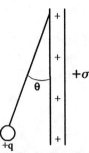

surface charge density σ suspends a small pith ball of mass m and charge $+q$ by a thread, as shown. (a) Derive an equation for the angle θ as a function of the parameters of the problem. (b) If $q = 1.0\mu$ C, $\sigma = 10$ nC/m^2, and $m = 0.10$ g, calculate the angle θ. (c) Calculate the tension in the thread.

Answer: (a) $\theta = \tan^{-1}[q\sigma/2mg\epsilon_0]$; (b) 30°; (c) 1.13×10^{-3} N

26. An electric dipole moment, p, consists of two equal

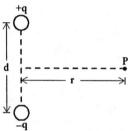

but opposite charges, $+q$ and $-q$, separated by a distance, d, i.e., $p = qd$. (a) Derive an equation for the field at point P at right angles to the midpoint of the dipole in terms of the electric dipole moment and problem parameters. (b) Calculate the electric dipole moment of a proton and electron separated by 0.10 mm. (c) Calculate the electric field for $r = 1.0$ mm.

Answer: (a) $E = 8$ kp/$(d^2 + 4r^2)^{3/2}$, downward; (b) 1.60×10^{-23} Cm; (c) 1.44×10^{-4} N/m, downward

27. A spherical geometry has 4 charges of $-q$ placed

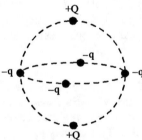

90° apart on the equatorial plane and 2 charges of $+Q$ placed at the poles, as shown. (a) Derive an equation for the charges Q in terms of q so that there is no net forces on Q. (b) If one $+Q$ is removed, derive an equation for Q in terms of q so that the electric field in the vacated position is zero.

Answer: (a) $Q = 4\sqrt{2}q$; (b) $Q = 4\sqrt{2}q$

28. Two very long coaxial cylinders of 1.0 cm and 3.0 cm radii have linear charge densities of $+5.0\mu$ C/m and -7.5μ C/m on the inner and outer cylinders, respectively. (a) Calculate the electric field midway between the cylinders. (b) Calculate the electric field at $r = 5.0$ cm.

Answer: (a) 4.5×10^6 N/C, outward; (b) 9.0×10^5 N/C, inward

104

29. Two concentric spheres of 1.0 cm and 3.0 cm radii have surface charge densities of $+5.0\mu$ C/m^2 and -7.5μ C/m^2 on the inner and outer spheres, respectively. (a) Calculate the electric field midway between the spheres. (b) Calculate the electric field at $r = 5.0$ cm.

Answer: (a) 1.41×10^5 N/C, outward; (b) 2.82×10^5 N/C, inward

30. One useful model of the electron views it as a homogeneous sphere of charge of radius a_0. (a) Derive an equation for the electric field at a distance $r < a_0$. (b) Derive an equation for the electric field at a distance $r > a_0$.

Answer: (a) $E = -er/4\pi\epsilon_0 a_0^3$, inward; (b) $E = -e/4\pi\epsilon_0 r^2$, inward

31. Calculate the magnitude of the electric field at the center of the square with sides 20cm long if the corners, taken in rotation, have charges of 1.0μC, 2.0μC, 3.0μC and 4.0μC.

Answer: E=1.3×10^6N/C

32. An electron with speed $v_0 = 2.4 \times 10^6$m/s is traveling parallel to an electric field of magnitude $E = 8.4 \times 10^3$N/C. (a) How far will it travel before it stops? (b) How much time will elapse before it returns to its starting position?

Answer: (a) 1.9×10^{-3}m; (b) 3.2×10^{-9}s.

33. In the Millikan oil drop experiment for measuring the charge of an electron, an ionized droplet 1.4μ m in diameter and density 0.85 g/cm^3 is balanced against gravity by an electric field of 6.8×10^3 N/C. (a) Calculate the weight of the droplet. (b) Calculate the number of ionizing electrons on the droplet.

Answer: (a) 1.20×10^{-14} N(b) 11

34. A proton ($m = 1.67 \times 10^{-27}$ kg) is injected at an

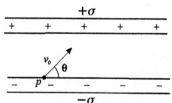

angle of 45° with a speed of 1.5×10^6 m/s into a region between two large non-conducting plates with equal but opposite charge densities $\sigma = 2.5\mu$ C/m^2, as shown. (a) Calculate the acceleration experienced by the proton. (b) If the plates are 2.3 cm apart, how close does the proton come to the upper plate?

Answer: (a) 2.70×10^{13} m/s^2; (b) 0.22 cm

CHAPTER 16

16.0 - MULTIPLE CHOICE QUESTIONS

1. If in the Millikan oil drop experiment the electric field is 6.8×10^3 N/C and the field plates (parallel to each other) are 1.5 cm apart, the potential difference is:

    a. 50 V
    b. 80 V
    c. 100 V
    d. 120 V
    e. None of the above

    Answer: 100 V

2. A large metal plate has a surface charge density of 0.175 μC/m^2. The spacing between 100 V equipotential lines at the center of the plate is:

    a. 5 mm
    b. 7.5 mm
    c. 1.5 cm
    d. 2.5 cm
    e. None of the above

    Answer: 5 mm

3. A potential of 100 V is measured 90 cm from an isolated charge. The magnitude of the charge is:

    a. 1 nC
    b. 10 nC
    c. 100 nC
    d. 1 μC
    e. None of the above

    Answer: 10 nC

4. The potential at the center of a circle of radius 90 cm with three charges of +1 nC, -2 nC, and +3 nC placed 120° apart on the circumference is:

    a. 8 V
    b. 12 V
    c. 16 V
    d. 20 V
    e. None of the above

    Answer: 20 V

5. The amount of work required to bring +1 μC and -1 μC charges from infinity to 1.0 cm apart is:

    a. -0.60 J
    b. 0.90 J
    c. -1.20 J

d. 2.4 J
e. None of the above

Answer: None of the above

6. Three electrons are placed at the apexes of an equilateral triangle with 6.9 Å sides. The total electric potential energy of this assembly is:

a. 1×10^{-18} J
b. 2×10^{-24} J
c. 3×10^{-31} J
d. 1×10^{-38} J
e. None of the above

Answer: 1×10^{-18} J

7. The work required to move +2.5 mC of charge from a 10 V equipotential line to a 50 V equipotential line is:

a. 10 mJ
b. 100 mJ
c. 500 mJ
d. 1.0 J
e. None of the above

Answer: 100 mJ

8. The nucleus of Xenon (element 54) has a radius of about 6.1×10^{-15} m; thus, the potential at the surface of the nucleus is:

a. 0.5 MV
b. 0.8 MV
c. 5 MV
d. 13 MV
e. None of the above

Answer: 13 MV

9. Two 1.0 cm diameter circular metal plates have a 0.10 mm thick mica disk (dielectric constant 5.4) between them. The capacitance of the structure is:

a. 16 pF
b. 27 pF
c. 38 pF
d. 54 pF
e. None of the above

Answer: 38 pF

10. Two parallel plates are charged to a voltage of 50V. If the separation between the plates is 5.0cm what is the electric field between them?

a. 3000 V/m
b. 1000 V/m

c. 500 V/m
d. 5000 V/m
e. None of the above

Answer: 1000 V/m

11. Consider a parallel plate capacitor with plates of size 20cm $\times$ 3.0cm that are separated by a 1.0mm air gap. What is the charge on each plate if the capacitor is connected to a 12V battery?

   a. 0.64 nC
   b. 1.00 nC
   c. 1.32 nC
   d. 14.2 nC
   e. None of the above

Answer: 0.64 nC

12. A 50 μF electrolytic capacitor is connected to a 12 V battery. The total charge removed from the battery is:

   a. 500 μJ
   b. 600 μJ
   c. 720 μJ
   d. 1.2 mJ
   e. None of the above

Answer: 600 μJ

13. A 50 μF electrolytic capacitor is connected to a 12 V battery. The energy stored on the capacitor is:

   a. 1.2 mJ
   b. 2.5 mJ
   c. 3.6 mJ
   d. 7.2 mJ
   e. None of the above

Answer: 3.6 mJ

14. How many 1.0 μF capacitors must be connected in parallel to store 60 μC of charge when connected to a 12 V battery?

   a. 2
   b. 4
   c. 6
   d. 8
   e. None of the above

Answer: None of the above

15. How many 1.0 μF capacitors must be connected in series to store 1.5 μC of charge when connected to a 12 V battery?

   a. 2
   b. 4

c. 6
d. 8
e. None of the above

Answer: 8

16. How much energy is stored by eight 1.0 μF capacitors in parallel across a 12 V battery?

   a. 0.58 mJ
   b. 0.72 mJ
   c. 1.2 mJ
   d. 4.8 mJ
   e. None of the above

Answer: 0.58 mJ

17. How much energy is stored by five 1.0 μF capacitors in series across a 12 V battery?

   a. 6 μJ
   b. 14 μJ
   c. 28 μJ
   d. 60 μJ
   e. None of the above

Answer: 14 μJ

16.0 - PROBLEMS

18. An electric dipole consists of +1.5 μC and

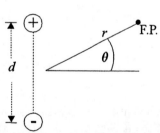

-1.5 μC charges separated by 8.5 mm. A field point (F.P.) is located 120 cm from the midpoint between the charges at an angle of 45°, as shown. (a) Calculate the difference between the distances from the minus and plus charges to the F.P. (b) Calculate the electric potential at the F.P. due to the dipole.
Answer: (a) 0.60 cm; (b) 56.4 V

19. A large plastic sheet has a surface charge density of +2.5 μC/m^2. (a) Calculate the work to place a +1.2 μC charge 1.75 m away on to the sheet. (b) Calculate the potential of the sheet if the potential at 1.75 m is taken as zero.
Answer: (a) 0.30 J; (b) 2.5 × 10^5 V

20. Four charges are located at the corners of a

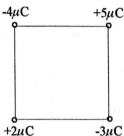

square with 10 cm sides, as shown. (a) Calculate the potential at the center of the square.(b) Calculate the potential at the midpoint between the +2 μC charge and the −4 μC charge.

Answer: (a) 0; (b) −2.0 × 10^5 V

21. Two large metal plates at +120 V and −60 V potentials are separated by 1.8 cm. (a) Calculate the electric field between the plates. (b) Calculate the time it takes an alpha particle (He nucleus, $m = 6.6 \times 10^{-27}$ kg), initially at rest, to move from the positive to the negative plate.

Answer: (a) 100 V/cm; (b) 2.7 μs

22. A solid metal sphere of 5 mm radius has a surface charge density of +16 μC/m^2. (a) Calculate the potential at the surface of the sphere. (b) Calculate the electric field at the surface of the sphere. (c) Calculate the potential and electric field at the center of the sphere.

Answer: (a) 9.0 × 10^3 V; (b) 1.8 × 10^6 V/m; (c) 9.0 × 10^3 V, 0 V/m

23. A solid metal sphere of 6 cm radius has a potential of 450 V. (a) Calculate the charge on the sphere. (b) Calculate the charge density on the sphere.

Answer: (a) 3.0 nC; (b) 66 nC/m^2

24. Three charges are brought from infinity and

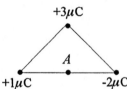

placed on the vertices of an equilateral triangle with 25 cm sides, as shown. (a) Calculate the work done. (b) Calculate the potential at point A.

Answer: (a) −0.18 J; (b) 5.3 × 10^4 V

25. Three charges are brought from infinity and

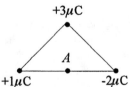

placed on the vertices of an equilateral triangle with 25 cm sides, as shown. (a) Calculate the work done in moving the +3 μC charge to point A. (b) Calculate the potential at the vacated site now.

Answer: (a) −0.11 J; (b) 8.9 × 10^4 V

26. A Van de Graaff accelerator has an isolated 1.0 m diameter sphere into which a small belt delivers negative charge at the rate of 0.25 mC/s into the inner shell against an average potential of -1.5 MV. (a) Calculate the minimum horse power of the motor that drives the belt. (b) Calculate the time it takes to charge the sphere to 10 MV.

Answer: (a) 0.50 hp; (b) 2.2 s

27. Three uncharged capacitors, $C_1 = 10\ \mu F$,

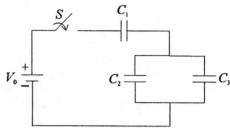

$C_2 = 4\ \mu F$, and $C_3 = 6\ \mu F$, are connected, as shown, to a voltage source, $V_0 = 12$ V, through a switch, S, which is closed. (a) Calculate the final voltage across C_2. (b) Calculate the total charge supplied by V_0.

Answer: (a) 6 V; (b) 60 μC

28. Three uncharged capacitors, $C_1 = 4\ \mu F$,

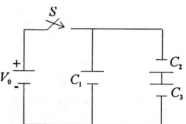

$C_2 = 10\ \mu F$, and $C_3 = 15\ \mu F$, are connected, as shown, to a voltage source, $V_0 = 12$ V, through a switch, S, which is closed. (a) Calculate the final voltage across C_2. (b) Calculate the total charge supplied by V_0.

Answer: (a) 7.2 V; (b) 120 μC

29. A 0.5 μF capacitor is charged to 24 V and then disconnected from the voltage source. A second capacitor is connected across the 0.5 μF capacitor and the final voltage is 16 V. (a) Calculate the value of the second capacitor. (b) If the second capacitor is actually two series capacitors, one of which is 1.0 μF, calculate the value of the other.

Answer: (a) 0.25 μF; (b) 0.33 μF

30. A parallel plate capacitor is constructed from

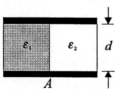

two metal plates of area, A, with two different materials of dielectric constants, ϵ_1 and ϵ_2, and equal areas and thicknesses, as shown. (a) Derive a formula for the capacitance of this structure. (b) If

$\epsilon_1 = 2.6, \epsilon_2 = 5.4, d = 0.01$ mm, $A = 100$ cm^2, calculate the energy stored by this structure when connected to a 12 V source.

Answer: (a) $(\epsilon_0 A/2d)(\epsilon_1 + \epsilon_2)$; (b) 2.55 μJ

31. A parallel plate capacitor is constructed from

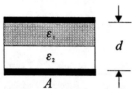

two metal plates of area, A, with two different materials of dielectric constants, ϵ_1 and ϵ_2, and equal areas and thicknesses, as shown. (a) Derive a formula for the capacitance of this structure. (b) If $\epsilon_1 = 2.6$, $\epsilon_2 = 5.4$, $d = 0.01$ mm, $A = 100$ cm^2, calculate the energy stored by this structure when connected to a 12 V source.

Answer: (a) $(2\epsilon_0 A/d)(\epsilon_1 \epsilon_2/\epsilon_1 + \epsilon_2)$; (b) 2.24 μJ

32. What is the electric potential 21.0cm from a 4.85μC point charge?.

Answer: 208kV

33. Dry air will break down if the electric field exceeds 3.0×10^6V/m. What anount of charge can be placed on a capacitor if the area of each plate is 20cm^2?

Answer: 53nC

34. A parallel plate capacitor of 100 cm^2 area and plate separation of 0.01 mm is filled (between the plates) with an unknown fluid and then charged from a 12 V source. The source is disconnected and the fluid is removed. The final voltage is 300 V. (a) Calculate the dielectric constant of the unknown fluid. (b) Calculate the field between the plates if the space is then filled with transformer oil ($\epsilon = 4.5$).

Answer: (a) 25; (b) 6.67×10^6 V/m

CHAPTER 17

17.0 - MULTIPLE CHOICE QUESTIONS

1. A current of 2.5 A flows through a 10 Ω resistor for 1.5 minutes. The number of electrons entering or leaving the resistor is:

    a. 1.4×10^{21}
    b. 2.5×10^{21}
    c. 7.4×10^{21}
    d. 2.8×10^{22}
    e. None of the above

    Answer: 1.4×10^{21}

2. Copper has a density of 8.96 g/cm^3 and atomic mass of 63.5. The number of conduction electrons per cm^3 is (one per atom in Cu):

    a. 2.4×10^{21}
    b. 4.2×10^{22}
    c. 8.5×10^{22}
    d. 1.2×10^{23}
    e. None of the above

    Answer: 8.5×10^{22}

3. If 1.6 mm diameter aluminum wire has a current of 2.9 A and 1.81×10^{23} el/cm^3, the drift velocity of conduction electrons is:

    a. 0.02 mm/s
    b. 0.05 mm/s
    c. 0.9 mm/s
    d. 1.2 mm/s
    e. None of the above

    Answer: 0.05 mm/s

4. 1.20 mm diameter tin wire carries a current of 3.67 A with drift velocity of the conduction electrons of 0.14 mm/s. The conduction electron density is:

    a. 2.1×10^{22}cm^{-3}
    b. 3.7×10^{22}cm^{-3}
    c. 8.6×10^{22}cm^{-3}
    d. 1.4×10^{23}cm^{-3}
    e. None of the above

    Answer: 1.4×10^{23}cm^{-3}

5. A 10 cm^2 area parallel plate capacitor has a 0.01 mm thick dielectric between the plates. If 100 V is applied, a current of 0.1 mA flows. The resistivity of the dielectric (in Ω-cm) is:

    a. 1.0×10^9

b. 3.5×10^9
c. 1.0×10^{10}
d. 3.5×10^{11}
e.   None of the above

Answer: 1.0×10^{10}

6.   0.51 mm diameter Nichrome wire (10^{-4} Ω-cm) is used as a heater element. If 115 V is used, the length of wire required for 1200 W of heat is:

   a.   180 cm
   b.   225 cm
   c.   280 cm
   d.   310 cm
   e.   None of the above

Answer: 225 cm

7.   Two wires, one of Cu the other of Al, are the same length. The ratio of the diameter of Cu to Al so that the wires have the same resistance is:

   a.   0.78
   b.   0.88
   c.   1.28
   d.   1.62
   e.   None of the above

Answer: 0.78

8.   The monitor display beam of a computer uses 0.24 mA. The number of electrons per second striking the screen is:

   a. 2.4×10^{13}
   b. 8.2×10^{13}
   c. 1.2×10^{14}
   d. 1.5×10^{15}
   e.   None of the above

Answer: 1.5×10^{15}

9.   972 wraps of 18 gauge (40 mils diameter) insulated copper wire is wound on a cylindrical form of 5 cm diameter for a single layer coil. The resistance of this coil is:

   a.   0.4 Ω
   b.   0.6 Ω
   c.   0.8 Ω
   d.   1.2 Ω
   e.   None of the above

Answer: 0.8 Ω

10.   A 5.1 m long wire of 1.2 mm diameter has a resistance of 2.0 Ω. The conductivity of the wire (per Ω-cm) is:

a. 1.2×10^4
b. 2.3×10^4
c. 8.2×10^4
d. 1.5×10^5
e. None of the above

Answer: 2.3×10^4

11. A 0.08 mm diameter Nichrome heating wire 1.8 m long is operated at 1700° K. The operating resistance of this wire is:

a. 360 Ω
b. 480 Ω
c. 560 Ω
d. 600 Ω
e. None of the above

Answer: 600 Ω

12. What is the resistance of a 40W automobile headlight designed for 12V?

a. 7.2Ω
b. 1.2Ω
c. 6.4Ω
d. 3.6Ω
e. None of the above

Answer: 3.6Ω

13. Suppose you want to connect your stereo system to a speaker. If the each wire must be 20m long, what must be the diameter of the wire you will need to use if you wnat to keep the resistance less than 0.10Ω per wire?

a. 1.1mm
b. 2.1mm
c. 1.1cm
d. 2.1cm
e. None of the above

Answer: 2.1mm

14. A 100 W, 115 V tungsten filament light bulb has a cold resistance of 8.6 Ω. The operating temperature is:

a. 1200° C
b. 1600° C
c. 2600° C
d. 3200° C
e. None of the above

Answer: 3200° C

15. The copper coils of the starter motor in a car draw 100 A initially, but this drops to 75 A as the coils heat up. The final temperature of the windings is:

a. 85° C
b. 95° C
c. 105° C
d. 120° C
e. None of the above

Answer: 105° C

16. At 12¢/KWH, how much does it cost to operate an electric space heater for 12 hours from a 115 V source if its hot resistance is 16 Ω?

a. $1.20
b. $1.30
c. $1.40
d. $1.50
e. None of the above

Answer: $1.20

17. A carbon cylindrical resistor of 2.0 mm diameter and 1.2 cm long is made from a composition with a resistivity of 26.2 Ω-cm. The power dissipated by the resistor when connected to a 6 V supply is:

a. 24 mW
b. 36 mW
c. 42 mW
d. 56 mW
e. None of the above

Answer: 36 mW

17.0 - PROBLEMS

18. In an electrohydrodynamic experiment, helium atoms of density $2 \times 10^{16}/cm^3$ are 50% ionized into alpha particles (He nuclei) and free electrons in a uniform electric field. The drift velocity of alpha particles and electrons is 12 m/s and 64 m/s, respectively. (a) Calculate the conduction electron current density. (b) Calculate the total current density.

Answer: (a) 20.5 A/cm^2; (b) 24.3 A/cm^2

19. Consider two conductors, one a 2.3 mm diameter copper wire the other a 2.6 cm I.D. hollow copper tube with 0.20 mm wall thickness. (a) Calculate the length ratio of the solid wire to hollow tube for the same resistance. (b) If the hollow tube is made of different material, so that the resistance per unit length is the same for both, calculate the resistivity of the tube material.

Answer: (a) 0.25; (b) 6.7×10^{-6} Ω cm

20. Aluminum (2.7 g/cm^3) and copper (9.0 g/cm^3) are to be used for telephone lines. (a) Calculate the ratio of the length of Al wire to Cu wire if the current densities are to be the same for a given voltage. (b) If the resistance per unit length is to be 0.25 mΩ/m, calculate the mass per unit length for Al and Cu.

Answer: (a) 0.61; (b) 300 g/m, 610 g/m

21. A 1500 W, 115 V Nichrome space heater operates at 1200° C. Calculate the length of 0.42 mm diameter wire used when the unit is constructed at 20° C.

Answer: 77 cm

22. About 7% of the electrical energy in a light bulb is converted to light. Consider five 100 W light bulbs of constant resistance. (a) Calculate the light power obtained from five bulbs connected in series across 115 V. (b) Calculate the light power obtained from five bulbs connected in parallel across 115 V.

Answer: (a) 1.4 W; (b) 35 W

23. A 10 m long cable consists of seven strands

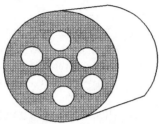

of 0.50 mm copper wire with insulation between, as shown. (a) Calculate the resistance of a strand. (b) Calculate the resistance of the cable.

Answer: (a) 0.87 Ω; (b) 0.12 Ω

24. A 3.0 A, 115 V immersion heater is put in 8 ounces of water at 15° C. (a) Calculate the time required for the water to come to a boil. (b) Calculate the additional time required to evaporate 4 ounces of water ($L_v = 2256$ J/g).

Answer: (a) 3 min., 54 s; .(b) 12 min., 22 s.

25. A Nichrome heater element measuring 4.0 Ω at 20° C is connected to a 12 V power source in a liquid which boils at 177° C and evaporates at the rate of 1.2 g/min. (a) Calculate the rate that heat energy is delivered to the liquid. (b) Calculate the heat of vaporization of the liquid.

Answer: (a) 3.1 J/s; (b) 1.54 kJ/g

26. A 12 V battery has an internal resistance of 0.005 Ω. (a) Calculate the electrical power delivered to a 2.0 horsepower, 12 V starter motor. (b) If the internal resistance increases to 0.01 Ω, calculate the power (in horsepower) that the starter motor can actually deliver. (Assume 100% efficiency.)

Answer: (a) 1350 W; (b) 1.64 hp

27. A 5 MeV beam 0.25 mm² in cross-section is composed of alpha particles (He nuclei, $m = 6.64 \times 10^{-27}$ kg) emitted in 10 μs pulses of 5 μA pulse current. (a) Calculate the number of particles in the pulse. (b) Calculate the charge density in the pulse.

Answer: (a) 1.56×10^8; (b) 1.3×10^{-12} C/cm³

28. A 330 KVA power plant delivers 25 A to a $\frac{3}{4}$ inch diameter copper transmission line for a city 500 miles away. (a) Calculate the voltage on the line at the city. (b) Calculate the rate at which heat energy is generated in the line.

Answer: (a) 12 kV; (b) 30 kJ/s

29. A thundercloud has an area of about 10^6 m^2 and forms a crude parallel plate capacitor with the ground below. If the air breaks down at about 5×10^6 V/m; (a) Calculate the charge in the lightning stroke (assume cloud completely discharges). (b) Calculate the current in the stroke if the discharge occurs in 0.05 s.

Answer: (a) 44.3 C; (b) 8850A

30. A 12 foot long lamp cord has 24 strands of #30 gauge copper wire (10 mils diameter). (a) Calculate the total resistance of the lamp cord. (b) Calculate the time it takes for the temperature to rise 30° C (assume no radiative heat loss) if the lamp draws 2 A and the density of Cu is 9.0 g/cm^3 and specific heat 0.386 J/g°C.

Answer: (a) 0.10 Ω; (b) 94 s

31. An unknown material is fabricated into a bar 2.5 mm × 4.0 mm and 2.0 m long. A current of 12 μA flows when 120 V is impressed across it. (a) Calculate the conductivity of the material. (b) Calculate the density of conduction electrons in this material if their drift velocity is measured as 0.15 mm/s.

Answer: (a) $2 \times 10^{-4} \Omega^{-1} cm^{-1}$; (b) $5 \times 10^{16} cm^{-3}$

32. An electric heater draws 15A on a 120V line. How much power does it use and how much does it cost per month (30 days) if it operates 3.0h per day and the electric power company charges $0.12 per kWh?

Answer: 1.8kW; $10.80

33. Electric power at 220V is applied to two different conductors made of the same material. One conductor is twice is long and twice as thick as the second. What is the ratio of the power transformed in the first relative to the second?

Answer: 2:1

34. Copper and aluminum wires of the same diameter are connected in series. (a) Calculate the fraction of the length which is aluminum if this compound wire has the same resistance as a copper wire of the same length but $\frac{4}{5}$ the diameter. (b) Calculate the multiple of length of the copper wire which has the same resistance as an alloy wire if they have the same diameter but the alloy wire is 25% Cu and 75% Al in length (assume resistivities add linearly).

Answer: (a) 0.87; (b) 1.48

CHAPTER 18

18.0 - MULTIPLE CHOICE QUESTIONS

1. A 100 Ω and a 200 Ω resistor are connected in parallel across a 200 V power source. The power dissipated by the resistors is:

    a. 6 W
    b. 12 W
    c. 16 W
    d. 20 W
    e. None of the above

    Answer: 6 W

2. A 33 Ω resistor is in series with a 56 Ω and a 81 Ω resistor in parallel. The current drawn from a 33 V battery is:

    a. 0.3 A
    b. 0.5 A
    c. 0.9 A
    d. 1.0 A
    e. None of the above

    Answer: 0.5 A

3. A pair of identical 12 V batteries, each storing 2×10^5 J of energy, are connected in parallel. How long can they supply 70 A?

    a. 4 min.
    b. 8 min.
    c. 16 min.
    d. 24 min.
    e. None of the above

    Answer: 8 min.

4. A pair of identical 12 V batteries, each storing 2×10^5 J of energy, are connected in series. How long can they supply 70 A?

    a. 4 min.
    b. 8 min.
    c. 16 min.
    d. 24 min.
    e. None of the above

    Answer: 4 min.

5. A 12 V (emf) car battery has a 0.02 Ω internal resistance. If it receives a 50 A quick charge, the voltage across the battery terminals during charging is:

    a. 11 V

b.　12 V
c.　13 V
d.　14 V
e.　None of the above

Answer: 13 V

6.　A 12 V (emf) car battery has a 0.02 Ω internal resistance. If it receives a 50 A quick charge, how much energy is stored in the battery after 5 minutes if it was previously uncharged?

　　a.　9.6×10^4 J
　　b.　1.2×10^5 J
　　c.　1.8×10^5 J
　　d.　2.0×10^5 J
　　e.　None of the above

Answer: 1.8×10^5 J

7.　Two batteries and two resistors are connected in a circuit, as shown. The voltage at A is:

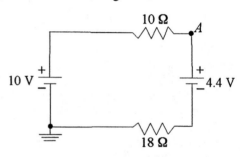

　　a.　8 V
　　b.　10 V
　　c.　12 V
　　d.　14 V
　　e.　None of the above

Answer: 8 V

8.　In the circuit shown, $V_1 = 12$ V, $V_2 = 8$ V, $V_3 = 4$ V, $R_1 = 100$ Ω, and $R_2 = 120$ Ω. The power dissipated in R_1 is:

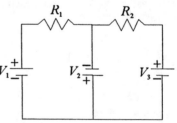

　　a.　1.8 W
　　b.　2.4 W
　　c.　3.6 W
　　d.　4.0 W
　　e.　None of the above

9. In the circuit shown, $V_1 = 12$ V, $V_2 = 8$ V, $V_3 = 4$ V, $R_1 = 100$ Ω, and $R_2 = 120$ Ω. The current through R_2 is:

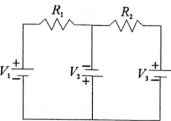

   a.   0.003 A
   b.   0.01 A
   c.   0.03 A
   d.   0.10 A
   e.   None of the above

Answer: 0.10 A

10. In the circuit shown, $V_0 = 10$ V, $R_1 = 100$ Ω, $R_2 = 49$ Ω, and $R_3 = 18$ Ω. The ammeter indicates:

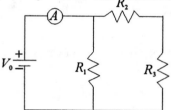

   a.   0.10 A
   b.   0.25 A
   c.   0.40 A
   d.   0.50 A
   e.   None of the above

Answer: 0.25 A

11. In the circuit shown, $V_1 = 12$ V, $V_2 = 18$ V, $V_3 = 6$ V, $R_1 = 10$ kΩ, and $R_2 = 1.2$ kΩ. The current through R_1 is:

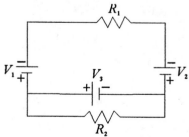

   a.   1.2 mA
   b.   1.8 mA
   c.   2.4 mA

d.   3.6 mA
e.   None of the above

Answer: 1.2 mA

12.   In the circuit shown, $V_1 = 12$ V, $V_2 = 18$ V, $V_3 = 6$ V, $R_1 = 10$ kΩ, and $R_2 = 1.2$ kΩ. The power dissipated in R_2 is:

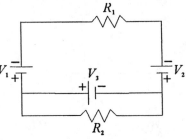

a.   12 mW
b.   18 mW
c.   24 mW
d.   30 mW
e.   None of the above

Answer: 30 mW

13.   In the circuit shown, the capacitor is initially charged to V_0 and $V_0 = 12$ V, $R = 100$ Ω, and $C = 100$ μF. The time for the voltage on C to decrease to 4 V after the switch is closed is:

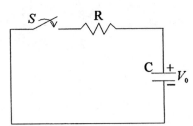

a.   9 ms
b.   10 ms
c.   11 ms
d.   12 ms
e.   None of the above

Answer: 11 ms

122

14. In the circuit shown, the capacitor is initially charged to V_0 and $V_0 = 12$ V, $R = 100 \, \Omega$, and $C = 100 \, \mu F$. The product, RC, is called the time constant. What percent of the initial voltage on C remains after 3 time constants?

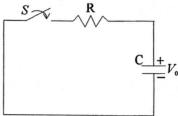

    a.   3%
    b.   5%
    c.   6%
    d.   12%
    e.   None of the above

Answer: 5%

15. Seven 8.0W Christmas tree light are connected in series to a 120V source. What is the resistance of each bulb?

    a.   72.3Ω
    b.   100Ω
    c.   21.4Ω
    d.   36.7Ω
    e.   None of the above

Answer: 36.7Ω

16. Three resistors are connected as follows: a 300Ω resistor is connected in parallel with the 700Ω resistor and they are connected in series with a 400Ω resistor. If the described combination of resistors is connected across the terminals of a 12V battery what current flows through the battery?

    a.   17mA
    b.   84mA
    c.   1.0mA
    d.   10mA
    e.   None of the above

Answer: 17mA

17. In the circuit shown, the capacitor is initially uncharged and $V_0 = 12$ V, $R = 100 \, \Omega$, and $C = 100 \, \mu F$. The time for the capacitor voltage to reach 10 V after the switch is closed is:

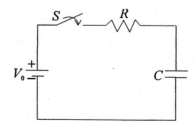

a.   6 ms
b.   11 ms
c.   16 ms
d.   18 ms
e.   None of the above

Answer: 18 ms

18.0 - PROBLEMS

18 .   A 0.12 mm diameter copper wire is clad with a 0.08 mm thick coating of aluminum. (a) Calculate the resistance of 1.0 m of this wire. (b) Calculate the conductance of this wire.

Answer: (a) 0.41 Ω; (b) 4.0 $\times$ 10^5/Ωcm

19.   A 12 V (emf) battery is connected to a 3.3 Ω wire wound resistor dissipating 30 W. (a) Calculate the terminal voltage of the battery. (b) Calculate the internal resistance of the battery.

Answer: (a) 9.95 V; (b) 0.68 Ω

20.   Two identical 9 V (emf) batteries are connected in

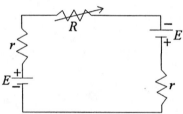

series with a variable resistor, as shown. The internal resistance of the batteries is 2.0 Ω. (a) If the variable resistor is set at 4.0 Ω, calculate the power dissipated by it. (b) If the variable resistor is set at 3.0 Ω, calculate the power dissipated by it. (c) If the variable resistor is set at 5.0 Ω, calculate the power dissipated by it.

Answer: (a) 20.25 W; (b) 19.84 Wl (c) 20 W

21.   Two identical 9 V (emf) batteries are connected in

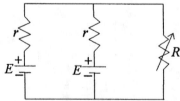

parallel with a variable resistor, as shown. The internal resistance of the batteries is 4.0 Ω. (a) If the variable resistor is set at 2.0 Ω, calculate the power dissipated by it. (b) If the variable resistor is set at 1.0 Ω, calculate the power dissipated by it. (c) If the variable resistor is set at 3.0 Ω, calculate the power dissipated by it.

Answer: (a) 10.13 W; (b) 9.0 W; (c) 9.72 W

22. A $\frac{1}{4}$ horsepower go-cart motor is powered by a 24 V (emf) battery with a 0.10 Ω internal resistance. (a) Calculate the current delivered by the battery to the motor. (b) Calculate the rate of heat generation in the battery when in use.

Answer: (a) 8.0 A (b) 6.4 J/s

23. An ideal voltmeter and ammeter are connected,

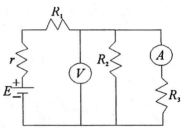

as shown, in a circuit where $E = 12$ V, $r = 1.0$ Ω, $R_1 = 10$ Ω, $R_2 = 33$ Ω, and $R_3 = 56$ Ω. (a) Calculate the voltage reading of the voltmeter. (b) Calculate the current reading of the ammeter.

Answer: (a) 7.84 V; (b) 0.14 A

24. In the circuit shown, $V_1 = 12$ V,

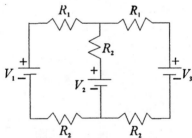

$V_2 = 9$ V, $V_3 = 3$ V, $R_1 = 12$ Ω, and $R_2 = 18$ Ω. (a) Calculate the current through V_1. (b) Calculate the current through V_3. (c) Calculate the current through V_2.

Answer: (a) 0.127 A; (b) 0.173 A; (c) 0.0455 A

25. In the circuit shown, $V_0 = 24$ V,

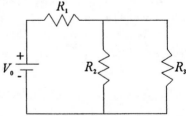

$R_1 = 12$ Ω, and $R_2 = 18$ Ω. (a) If the power supply delivers 24 W, calculate the value of R_3. (b) Calculate the current through R_3.

Answer: (a) 36 Ω; (b) 0.33 A

26. For the circuit shown, (a) derive an

125

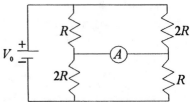

equation for the current through the ammeter in terms of the parameters given. (b) If the ammeter is replaced by a voltmeter, derive an equation for the voltage across the voltmeter in terms of the parameters given.

Answer: (a) $I_A = V_0/4R$; (b) $V_V = V_0/3$

27.   Some circuits have current sources

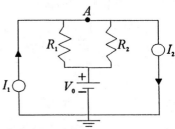

(instead of voltage sources) which are infinite resistance sources, such as shown, where $I_1 = 0.50$ A, $I_2 = 0.25$ A, $V_0 = 4.5$ V, $R_1 = 47$ Ω, and $R_2 = 81$ Ω. (a) Calculate the current through R_1. (b) Calculate the voltage at point A.

Answer: (a) 0.158 A; (b) 11.9 V

28.   A high way warning flasher is shown

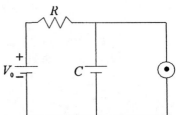

with a gas lamp which is an open circuit until it "breaks down" or ionizes at a voltage, V_B, when it then becomes a short circuit discharging the capacitor instantaneously (almost). If $V_0 = 100$ V, $V_B = 72$ V, and $C = 1.0$ μF, (a) calculate R for a 5 s flash interval. (b) Calculate the energy delivered by C to the bulb each flash.

Answer: (a) 3.9 MΩ; (b) 2.6 mJ

29.   In the circuit shown, the switch is at A

126

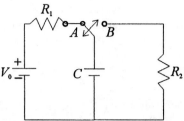

until the current stops flowing and then it is moved to B until the current stops flowing then back to A, etc. If $R_1 = 56$ kΩ, $R_2 = 18$ kΩ, and $C = 120$ μF, (a) calculate the time for the current to drop to 1% of its initial value when the switch is moved to B. (b) Calculate the time for the current to drop to 1% of its initial value when the switch is moved back to A.

Answer: (a) 9.95 s; (b) 31 s

30.   The value of a resistor, R, is to be found

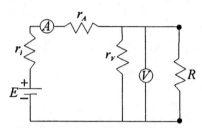

by measuring the current and voltage with an ammeter of internal resistance, r_A, and a voltmeter of resistance, r_V, as shown. The emf, E, has an internal resistance, r_i. (a) Derive a formula for the voltage that will be indicated by the voltmeter in terms of the parameters given. (b) Derive a formula for the current that will be indicated by the ammeter in terms of the parameters given

Answer: (a) $V = E[1 - (r_i + r_A)/R_T]$; (b) $I = E/R_T$; $R_T = \left(r_i + r_A + \frac{R r_V}{R + r_V}\right)$

31.   The value of a resistor, R, is to be found

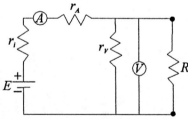

by measuring the current and voltage with an ammeter of internal resistance, r_A, and a voltmeter of resistance, r_V, as shown. The emf, E, has an internal resistance, r_i. Let $E = 9.0$ V, $r_i = 0.10$ Ω, $r_A = 2.0$ Ω, $r_V = 10$ kΩ, and $R = 1.20$ kΩ. (a) Calculate the measure value of R using this circuit. (b) Calculate the percent error in the measurement.

Answer: (a) 1.07 kΩ; (b) 11%

32.   A heart pacemaker is designed to operate at 70 beats/min using a 4.0μF capacitor. What value of resistance should be used if the pacemaker is to fire when the voltage reaches 63% of maximum?

Answer: 210kΩ

33. Suppose you want to run some apparatus that is 150m away from the electrical outlet. Each of the wires connecting the apparatus to the 120V source has resistance of 0.0065Ω/m. (a) If your apparatus draws 3.0A what will be the voltage drop across the connecting wires? (b) What will be voltage applied to your apparatus?

Answer: (a) 5.85V (b) 114.15V

34. A rheostat of length, l, and resistance

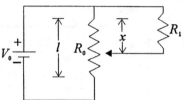

$R_0 = 1.8$ kΩ, has a resistor, $R_1 = 5.4$ kΩ, connected across it, as shown. x is the distance the wiper is down from the top. (a) Derive an expression for the current from the source, $V_0 = 18$ V, in terms of the fractional setting of the rheostat, x/l. (b) Evaluate the expression obtained for $(x/l) = 1/3$.

Answer: (a) $I = 10^{-2}[((x/l) + 3)/(3 + (x/l) - (x/l)^2)]$; (b) 10.3 mA

CHAPTER 19

19.0 - MULTIPLE CHOICE QUESTIONS

1. Two 115 V power lines, each carrying 100 A to the east, are 40 cm apart. The magnetic field density midway between the lines is:

    a. 5×10^{-6} T
    b. 1×10^{-5} T
    c. 5×10^{-5} T
    d. 1×10^{-4} T
    e.   None of the above

    Answer: None of the above

2. Two 115 V power lines, each carrying 100 A to the east, are 40 cm apart. The force per meter between the lines is:

    a. 5×10^{-5} N
    b. 1×10^{-4} N
    c. 5×10^{-3} N
    d. 1×10^{-2} N
    e.   None of the above

    Answer: 5×10^{-3} N

3. A flat coil of 100 turns and 25 cm diameter has a magnetic field of 5×10^{-3} T at its center. The current in the wire is:

    a.   5 A
    b.   10 A
    c.   50 A
    d.   100 A
    e.   None of the above

    Answer: 10 A

4. A 10 cm long solenoid has 500 turns of wire and is designed to cancel the earth's magnetic field $(2.5 \times 10^{-5}$ T) at its center. The current required is:

    a.   0.2 mA
    b.   0.4 mA
    c.   1.2 mA
    d.   4 mA
    e.   None of the above

    Answer: 4 mA

5. A 1.0 keV electron moving horizontally enters a uniform vertical magnetic field of 1.8×10^{-3} T. The diameter of the circle of its resulting motion is:

    a.   3 cm

b.   6 cm
c.   12 cm
d.   18 cm
e.   None of the above

Answer: 12 cm

6.   The plane of an 80 turn circular coil of 6 cm diameter carrying 7.5 A makes an angle of 60° with a 1.2 T magnetic field. The torque exerted on the coil is:

a.   1.0 N
b.   1.7 N
c.   2.4 N
d.   3.4 N
e.   None of the above

Answer: 1.0 N

7.   A stream of electrons in a vacuum tube are observed to orbit in a 4 cm diameter circle in a 1.6×10^{-3} T magnetic field. The electrons' energy is:

a.   45 eV
b.   90 eV
c.   180 eV
d.   240 eV
e.   None of the above

Answer: 90 eV

8.   An electric field of 250 V/m and a normal magnetic field 0.25 T act on an electron so as to produce no deflection. The minimum speed of the electron is:

a.   100 m/s
b.   250 m/s
c.   500 m/s
d.   1000 m/s
e.   None of the above

Answer: 1000 m/s

9.   The magnetic field is 1.0 mT 18 cm from a long straight wire. The current in the wire is:

a.   300 A
b.   600 A
c.   900 A
d.   1200 A
e.   None of the above

Answer: 900 A

10.   A 4.0 mm diameter wire carries 72 A. The magnetic field 1.5 mm from the axis of the wire is:

a.   2.7 mT
b.   5.4 mT
c.   7.2 mT

d. 9.6 mT
e. None of the above

11. A proton ($m = 1.67 \times 10^{-27}$ kg) traveling at 30° with respect to a 5.2 mT magnetic field line experiences an acceleration of 1.0×10^{12} m/s^2. Its speed is:

    a. 4×10^6 m/s
    b. 7×10^6 m/s
    c. 8×10^6 m/s
    d. 1.2×10^7 m/s
    e. None of the above

12. An alpha particle beam (He nuclei, $m = 6.64 \times 10^{-27}$ kg) traveling at 5.8×10^6 m/s enters a normal magnetic field region and reverses direction passing back through a port 1.2 m from the first. The magnetic field density is:

    a. 0.10 T
    b. 0.20 T
    c. 0.30 T
    d. 0.40 T
    e. None of the above

13. A wire formed into an equilateral triangle with 10 cm sides carries 30 A of current and the plane of the triangle makes an angle of 30° with a 0.8 T magnetic field. The torque exerted on the triangle is:

    a. 0.09 Nm
    b. 1.2 Nm
    c. 1.6 Nm
    d. 2.0 Nm
    e. None of the above

14. A wire carrying 30A current has length of 12cm between the pole faces of a magnet at an angle of 60°. The magnetic field is approximately uniform at 0.90T. Ignoring the magnetic field beyond the poles what is the force on the wire?

    a. 3.1N
    b. 2.8N
    c. 1.4N
    d. 5.6N
    e. None of the above

15. Carbon atoms of atomic mass 12.0 u are found to be mixed with another, unknown, element In a mass spectrometer, the carbon traverses a path of radius 22.4 cm and the path of the unknown element has

radius of 26.2cm. Assuming that the charge of the charge of the carbon ion is the same as the charge of the unknown element's ion what is the mass of the unknown element?

    a.   17.0 u
    b.   12.0 u
    c.   14.0 u
    d.   15.0 u
    e.   None of the above

Answer: 14.0 u

16.   A square loop of wire with 25 cm sides carries 16 A of current. Half of the loop is in a normal magnetic field of 250 mT. The force on the loop is:

    a.   0.3 N
    b.   0.6 N
    c.   0.8 N
    d.   1.0 N
    e.   None of the above

Answer: 1.0 N

17.   A long wire at right angles to the horizontal $(N - S)$ earth's magnetic field (45 μT) carries a current of 225 A to the west. The magnetic field density 1.0 m below the wire is:

    a.   0
    b.   45 μT
    c.   90 μT
    d.   135 μT
    e.   None of the above

Answer: 0

19.0 - PROBLEMS

18.   A proton moves with a particular KE in a circular orbit in a uniform magnetic field. An alpha particle moves in a circular orbit of the same radius. (a) Derive a formula for the KE of the alpha particle in terms of the KE of the proton and their associated masses. (b) Derive a formula for the speed of the alpha particle in terms of the speed of the proton and their associated kinetic energies.

Answer: (a) $KE_\alpha = 4(m_p/m_\alpha)KE_p$; (b) $v_\alpha = 1/2(KE_\alpha/KE_p)v_p$

19.   A proton moves with a particular KE in a circular orbit in a uniform magnetic field. An alpha particle moves in a circular orbit of the same radius. $m_p = 1.67 \times 10^{-27}$, $m_\alpha = 6.64 \times 10^{-27}$ kg, and the proton's KE is 334 keV. (a) Calculate the KE of the alpha particle for the same radius orbit as the proton. (b) Calculate the speed of the alpha particle for the same radius orbit.

Answer: (a) 334 keV; (b) 4×10^6 m/s

20.   A 230 eV electron enters a 170 μT magnetic

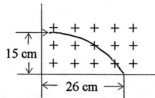

field 15 cm above and normal to a wall and strikes this surface 26 cm away, as shown. (a) Calculate the angle, with respect to the normal to this surface, that the electron strikes this surface. (b) Calculate the magnetic field required for the electron to strike this surface at normal incidence.

Answer: (a) 30°; (b) 340 μT

21. A 12 A current, I, flows in a long conductor.

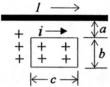

A rectangular loop, $b = 10$ cm, $c = 15$ cm, is placed $a = 5$ cm away, as shown. A 2.5 A current, i, flows clockwise around the loop. (a) Calculate the force on the loop. (b) Is it attractive or repulsive?

Answer: (a) 1.2×10^{-5} N; (b) Attractive

22. Three parallel conductors, in a plane, each carrying 120 A in the same direction are spaced 25 cm apart. (a) Which conductor experiences the largest force? Calculate this force per unit length. (b) Which conductor experiences the least force? Calculate this force per unit length.

Answer: (a) Outside, 1.73×10^{-2} N/m; (b) Inside, 0

23. Four conductors are arranged in a square,

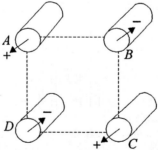

12 cm on a side, as shown, and carrying the following currents: A (120 A out), B (60 A in), C (90 A out), D (80 A in). Calculate the forces per unit length on conductors: (a) A; (b) B; (c) C; (d) D.

Answer:(a) -1.5×10^{-2} N/m; (b) -1.5×10^{-2} N/m; (c) -0.83×10^{-2} N/m; (d) -2.2×10^{-2} N/m

24. Two long lines 10 cm apart carry equal

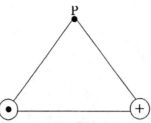

currents of 25 A but in opposite directions. A point, P, is 10 cm from each conductor, as shown. (a) Calculate the vertical component of field at point P. (b) Calculate the horizontal component of field at point P.

Answer: (a) 50 μT; (b) 0

25. Four long conductors are arranged in a

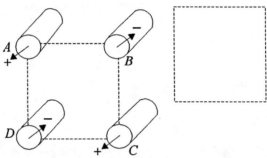

square with 10 cm sides, as shown. Each conductor carries 25 A but in different directions, as shown. (a) Calculate the vertical component of field at the center, C. (b) Calculate the horizontal component of field at the center, C.

Answer: (a) 200 μT; (b) 0

26. Two conductors, d apart, carry equal but

oppositely directed currents, as shown. Point P is equidistant from each conductor and a distance, x, from a line joining them. (a) Derive an equation for the magnitude of magnetic field at point P in terms of the parameters given and constants. (b) What is the direction of the magnetic field at point P for the currents shown.

Answer: (a) $B = 4\mu_0 I x/\pi(4x^2 + d^2)$; (b) To the right

27. If an infinitely long wire has a field of

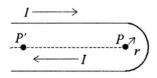

134

$\mu_0 I/2\pi r$ then a semi-infinitely long wire has a field of $\mu_0 I/4\pi r$. 25 A current flows in two long wires connected by a semi-circular bend of radius 10 mm, as shown. (a) Calculate the field at P' midway between the wires. (b) Calculate the field at P at the center of the semi-circular bend.

Answer: (a) 1.0 mT; (b) 1.28 mT

28. An N turn circular loop of wire of area A

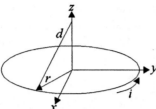

carries a current, i, as shown. This loop has a magnetic field on the z-axis given as $B = \mu_0 \mu/2\pi d^3$ where μ is the magnetic dipole moment given as $\mu = Ni$ A. If $N = 100$ turns, $i = 5$ A, and the loop is 25 mm in diameter, (a) calculate the magnetic dipole moment magnitude and direction. (b) Calculate the field 15 mm above the plane of the loop.

Answer: (a) 0.24 Am^2, up; (b) 6.6 mT

29. Two concentric single turn current loops of radii r_1 and r_2 carry currents i_1 and i_2, respectively. (a) Derive an equation for the magnetic dipole moment of this combination if both currents are equal and clockwise. (b) Derive an equation for the magnetic dipole moment if both currents are equal but i_1 is clockwise and i_2 is counterclockwise. (c) Evaluate (a) and (b) for $i_1 = i_2 = 10$ A and $r_1 = 10$ mm, $r_2 = 25$ mm.

Answer: (a) $\mu = i_1 \pi r_1^2 + i_2 \pi r_2^2$ (b) $\mu = i_1 \pi r_1^2 - i_2 \pi r_2^2$ (c) 2.3×10^{-2} Am^2, -1.6×10^{-2} Am^2

30. A mass spectrometer is used to monitor air polutants. It is difficult, however, to separate molecules with nearly equal mass such as CO (28.0106 u) and N$_2$ (28.0134 u). How large a radius of curvature must a spectrometer have if these two molecules are to be separated on the film by 0.33mm?

Answer: 1.65m

31. A vertical straight wire carrying 9.0A current exerts an attractive force per unit length of 7.0×10^{-4}N/m an a second wire 8.0cm away. What current (magnitude and the direction) flows in the second wire?

Answer: 31A in the same direction!

32. A 0.5 A current flows clockwise in a wire

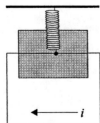

loop suspended on a spring of constant 10 kg/s^2 which is extended 1.5 mm due to the weight of the loop, as shown. If 20 cm of the wire is in a magnetic field (hatched area), (a) calculate the weight of the wire loop. (b) Calculate the magnitude and direction of the field to relax the spring to its rest position.

Answer: (a) 1.5×10^{-2} N; (b) 150 mT, into page

33. The potential energy of a magnetic dipole in a field is $Um = -\mu B \cos\theta$ where θ is the angle between the dipole and field. A flat coil 18 mm in diameter and 150 turns of wire carries 100 μA of current. The plane of the coil makes an angle of 60° with 250 mT magnetic field. (a) Calculate the two possible energies of the dipole. (b) Calculate the magnitude of the torque on the coil.

Answer: (a) $\pm$ 0.83 μJ; (b) 0.48 μNm

34. A 10 g flat bar lays across two horizontal, parallel tracks 30 cm apart, with a 5 mT vertical field in between, to complete a circuit for current. (a) Calculate the current required to just start moving the bar if the coefficient of friction is 0.12. (b) Calculate the speed of the bar and distance traveled in 8 s if the current is 10 A.

Answer: (a) 7.8 A; (b) 2.6 m/s, 10.4 m

CHAPTER 20

20.0 - MULTIPLE CHOICE QUESTIONS

1.	A changing flux of 130 mT/s is normal to a 196 turn, 5.0 cm diameter loop of wire open at the ends. The induced emf is:

   a.	10 mV
   b.	25 mV
   c.	50 mV
   d.	75 mV
   e.	None of the above

   Answer: 50 mV

2.	The flux normal to an 8 turn loop of 25 cm^2 area and open at the ends changes, as shown. The induced emf at 1.0 ms is positive then the induced emf at 3.0 ms is:

   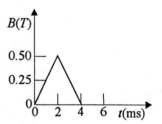

   a.	−5 V
   b.	5 V
   c.	−50 V
   d.	50 V
   e.	None of the above

   Answer: −5 V

3.	The flux normal to an 8 turn loop of 25 cm^2 area and open at the ends changes, as shown. If a 10 Ω resistor is placed across the open ends of the loop, the power dissipated in the resistor is:

   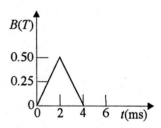

   a.	−2.5 W
   b.	2.5 W
   c.	−25 W
   d.	25 W
   e.	None of the above

   Answer: 2.5 W

4. An automobile with a 1.0 m radio antenna is traveling at 80 kph in the earth's magnetic field (45 μT). The induced emf in the antenna is:

    a.   1μV
    b.   10 μV
    c.   100 μV
    d.   1 mV
    e.   None of the above

Answer: 1 mV

5. A metal bar moves at 2.5 m/s on two conducting tracks 40 cm apart, as shown. The emf produced by a 0.5 T flux is:

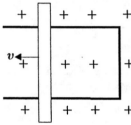

    a.   0.25 V
    b.   0.50 V
    c.   0.75 V
    d.   1.0 V
    e.   None of the above

Answer: 0.50 V

6. A metal bar moves at 2.5 m/s on two conducting tracks 40 cm apart, as shown. If the tracks have negligible resistance and the bar has a resistance of 0.125 Ω/cm, the current flowing is:

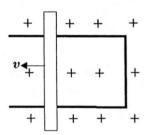

    a.   1 mA
    b.   10 mA
    c.   100 mA
    d.   1.0 Ac
    e.   None of the above

Answer: 100 mA

7. A metal bar moves at 2.5 m/s on two conducting tracks 40 cm apart, as shown. The force necessary to move the bar at 2.5 m/s is:

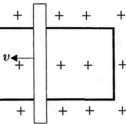

    a.   0.02 N
    b.   0.05 N
    c.   0.08 N
    d.   0.12 N
    e.   None of the above

Answer: 0.02 N

8. A 1000 turn, 10 cm long solenoid has a cross-sectional area of 1.6 cm². Its inductance is:

    a.   0.8 mH
    b.   1.2 mH
    c.   1.6 mH
    d.   2.0 mH
    e.   None of the above

Answer: 2.0 mH

9. A 1000 turn, 10 cm long solenoid has a cross-sectional area of 1.6 cm². The current is as shown. The emf induced in the inductor at 1.0 ms is:

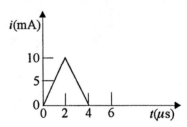

    a.   4 V
    b.   6 V
    c.   8 V
    d.   10 V
    e.   None of the above

Answer: 10 V

10. An inductor of 65 mH and 0.25 Ω resistance is suddenly connected to a 1.5 V battery. The time for the current to reach half its final value is:

    a.   0.10 s
    b.   0.18 s
    c.   0.25 s
    d.   0.68 s
    e.   None of the above

Answer: 0.18 s

11. An inductor of 65 mH and 0.25 Ω resistance is suddenly connected to a 1.5 V battery. How much energy does the inductor store after 1.0 s?

    a.   0.3 J
    b.   0.6 J
    c.   1.2 J
    d.   2.4 J
    e.   None of the above

Answer: 1.2 J

12. A 60 mH inductor is initially connected to a 12 V battery through $R_1 = 18$ Ω, as shown. The switch is instantaneously thrown to connect $R_2 = 36$ Ω. The initial output voltage, V_{out}, is:

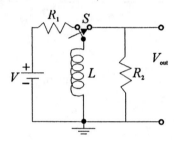

    a.   −6 V
    b.   −12 V
    c.   −18 V
    d.   −24 V
    e.   None of the above.

Answer: −24 V

13. A 60 mH inductor is initially connected to a 12 V battery through $R_1 = 18$ Ω, as shown. The switch is instantaneously thrown to connect $R_2 = 36$ Ω. The output voltage, V_{out}, after 1.2 ms is:

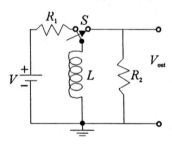

    a.   −6 V
    b.   −12 V
    c.   −18 V
    d.   −24 V
    e.   None of the above

Answer: −12 V

14. The flux linkage through a coil is 50 mWb when 2.5 A flows through it from a 6 V battery. The inductance of the coil is:

    a.   20 mH

b.   25 mH
c.   50 mH
d.   125 mH
e.   None of the above

Answer: 20 mH

15.   The armature of a 60Hz ac generator rotates in 0.15T magnetic field. If the area of the coil is 0.02 m², how many loops must the coil contain if the peak output is to be 170V?

a.   100 turns
b.   170 turns
c.   150 turns
d.   514 turns
e.   None of the above

Answer: 150 turns

16.   The armature windings of a dc motor have a resistence of 5.0Ω. The motor is connected to a 120V line and when a motor reaches full speed against its normal load, the counter emf is 108V. What is the current through the motor when it reaches full speed?

a.   2.4A
b.   24A
c.   12A
d.   1.0A
e.   None of the above

Answer: 2.4A

17.   The flux linkage through a coil is 50 mWb when 2.5 A flows through it from a 6 V battery. How long after the coil was connected to the battery was the flux 25 mWb?

a.   4.2 ms
b.   5.8 ms
c.   6.7 ms
d.   8.4 ms
e.   None of the above

Answer: 5.8 ms

20.0 - PROBLEMS

18.   An AC generator consists of a 120 turn loop

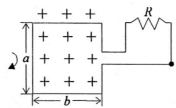

with $a = 5$ cm, $b = 15$ cm rotating at 60 cps in a 0.50 T flux, as shown. A 144 Ω resistor is the load. (a) Calculate the peak emf, E_0. (b) If the rms emf (average) is $E = E_0/\sqrt{2}$, calculate the power dissipated in the resistor.

141

19.   A 100 A current source sends current down two

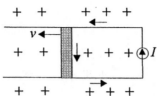

parallel tracks 10 cm apart and through a 100 g sliding bar, as shown. A flux of 2.5 T is normal to the plane of the tracks. If the bar starts from rest; (a) calculate its speed after traveling 45 m on a frictionless track. (b) Calculate the time it takes to travel 45 m from rest.

Answer: (a) 150 m/s; (b) 0.60 s

20.   A 50 mH inductor is switched to a and then

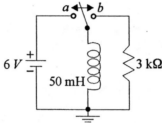

instantaneously to b 25 ms later, as shown. (a) With switch on a, show that the current increases linearly with time as $i = (V/L)t$.(b) Calculate the flux in the inductor after 25 ms. (c) Calculate the voltage at b the instant the switch is thrown to b.

Answer: (b) 0.15 Wb;   (c) −9.0 kV

21.   A 50 mH inductor is switched to a and then

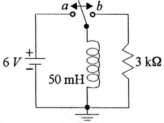

instantaneously to b 25 ms later, as shown. (a) calculate the voltage at b after 25 μs at position b. (b) Calculate the time for the current to decrease to 10 mA.

Answer: (a) −2.0 kV; (b) 95 μs

22.   A current source is turned on at $t = 0$, (a) By

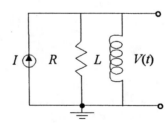

considering asymptotic values of $V(t)$, write an expression for $V(t)$. (b) If $I = 250$ mA, $R = 100\ \Omega$, and $L = 50\ \mu$H, calculate $V(t)$ after 1.0 μs.

Answer: (a) $V = IR \exp(-Rt/L)$; (b) 3.4 V

23. For the circuit shown, $V = 9$ V, $R_1 = 120\ \Omega$,

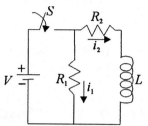

$R_2 = 30\ \Omega$, and $L = 180\ \mu$H. (a) Calculate i_2 after the switch is closed 6 μs. (b) Calculate the ratio of the power dissipated in R_1 to that in R_2 after 12 μs.

Answer: (a) 190 mA; (b) 0.33

24. For the circuit shown, $V = 9$ V, $R_1 = 120\ \Omega$,

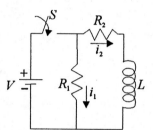

$R_2 = 30\ \Omega$, and $L = 180\ \mu$H. The switch is reopened after being closed for 1 ms. (a) Calculate the voltage across the inductor the instant the switch is opened. (b) Calculate the time for the inductor flux to decay to 10 μWb.

Answer: (a) 45 V; (b) 2.0 μs

25. For the circuit shown at 120 μs after the

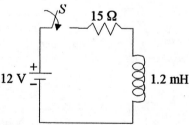

switch is closed, (a) calculate the instantaneous rate at which the resistor dissipates energy. (b) Calculate the instantaneous rate at which the inductor is storing energy. (c) Calculate the energy stored by the inductor flux.

Answer: (a) 5.8 J/s; (b) 1.66 J/s; (c) 230 μJ/s

26. The emf across a 25 μH inductor is shown.

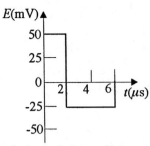

(a) Calculate the maximum current through the inductor if the current is zero at $t = 0$. (b) Calculate the energy stored in the inductor flux at $t = 4\ \mu s$.

Answer: (a) 4.0 mA; (b) 50 μJ

27. A 1.2 mm diameter copper wire has a resistance of 0.15 Ω/m and carries a 2.5 A current. (a) Calculate the electric energy density on the surface of the wire. (b) Calculate the magnetic energy density on the surface of the wire.

Answer: (a) 0.62 pJ/m^3; (b) 0.28 J/m^3

28. A 10 cm long solenoid of 1200 turns has a cross-sectional area of 3.2 cm^2. (a) Calculate the inductance of the solenoid. (b) Calculate the axial flux density of the solenoid for 2.5 A current. (c) Calculate the axial magnetic energy density for 2.5 A current.

Answer: (a) 5.8; (b) 38 mT; (c) 57 J/m^3

29. From the definition of self emf of an inductor, derive an equation for the equivalent inductance of two or more inductors in series.

Answer: $L_{eq} = L_1 + L_2 + ...$

30. From the definition of self emf of an inductor, derive an equation for the equivalent inductance of two or more inductors in parallel.

Answer: $1/L_{eq} = 1/L_1 + 1/L_2 + ...$

31. A square coil of side 5.0cm contains 100 loops and is positioned perpendicular to a uniform 0.60T magnetic field. It is quickly and uniformly pulled from the field (moving perpendicularly to the magnetic field) to a region where the magnetic field drops abruptly to zero. If it takes 0.10s for the whole coil to reach the zero magnetic field region, how much energy is dissipated in the coil if its resistance is 100Ω?

Answer: 2.3mJ

32. Calculate the selfinductance of a solenoid coil containing 100 turns of wire and length of 5.0cm if the diamater of a coil is 0.3cm. What is the selfinductance of the same coil if an iron core with relative magnetic permitivity of 4000 is used?

Answer: 7.5μH; 30mH

33. A magnetometer consists of a 100 turn, 3.0 cm diameter loop of wire rotating at 4800 rpm and an rms voltage detector (peak emf/$\sqrt{2}$). (a) Calculate the reading in millivolts for the earth's magnetic field (45 μT) normal to the axis of rotation of the loop. (b) If the instrument's sensitivity is 10 μV, calculate the smallest flux it can detect.

Answer: (a) 1.1 mV; (b) 0.40 μT

34. A single loop of 25 cm^2 area is moving to the

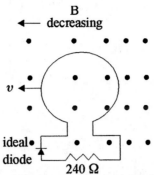

left at 1.8 m/s in a decreasing magnetic flux (3.6 Wb/m), as shown. (a) Calculate the power dissipated in the resistor. (b) If the loop reverses direction and moves to the right at 1.8 m/s, calculate the power dissipated in the resistor.

Answer: (a) 0;   (b) 1.1 μW

CHAPTER 21

21.0 - MULTIPLE CHOICE QUESTIONS

1.   A 33 μF capacitor is connected across a 115 V AC wall outlet. Its reactance is:

        a.   30 Ω
        b.   60 Ω
        c.   80 Ω
        d.   120 Ω
        e.   None of the above

                                                        Answer: 80 Ω

2.   An 80 mH inductor is connected across a 115 V AC wall outlet. Its reactance is:

        a.   30 Ω
        b.   60 Ω
        c.   80 Ω
        d.   120 Ω
        e.   None of the above

                                                        Answer: 30 Ω

3.   The impedance of a 120 Ω resistor, a 33 μF capacitor, and an 80 mH inductor in series and connected across a 115 V AC wall outlet is:

        a.   60 Ω
        b.   80 Ω
        c.   120 Ω
        d.   130 Ω
        e.   None of the above

                                                        Answer: 130 Ω

4.   A 120 Ω resistor, a 33 μF capacitor, and an 80 mH inductor in series and connected across a 115 V AC wall outlet. The peak current that flows is:

        a.   0.6 A
        b.   0.88 A
        c.   1.25 A
        d.   1.50 A
        e.   None of the above

                                                        Answer: 1.25 A

5.   A 120 Ω resistor, a 33 μF capacitor, and an 80 mH inductor in series and connected across a 115 V AC wall outlet. The power dissipated in the resistor is:

        a.   94 W
        b.   101 W
        c.   133 W
        d.   188 W
        e.   None of the above

                                                        Answer: 94 W

6. A 120 Ω resistor, a 33 μF capacitor, and an 80 mH inductor in series and connected across a 115 V AC wall outlet. The power factor is:

    a.   0.88
    b.   0.92
    c.   0.94
    d.   0.96
    e.   None of the above

Answer: 0.92

7. The value of an inductor which has the same reactance of a 1.0 μF capacitor at 1000 Hz is:

    a.   1.0 mH
    b.   25 mH
    c.   160 mH
    d.   1.0 H
    e.   None of the above

Answer: 25 mH

8. A transformer has 150 mA peak current in a 120 turn primary winding. The peak current induced in the 180 turn shorted secondary winding is:

    a.   100 mA
    b.   120 mA
    c.   180 mA
    d.   225 mA
    e.   None of the above

Answer: 100 mA

9. A 115 V AC electric motor has an AC resistance of 33 Ω and an inductive reactance of 48 Ω under full load. The peak current drawn is:

    a.   1.2 A
    b.   1.8 A
    c.   2.4 A
    d.   2.8 A
    e.   None of the above

Answer: 2.8 A

10. A 115 V AC electric motor has an AC resistance of 33 Ω and an inductive reactance of 48 Ω under full load. The average power used by the motor under full load is:

    a.   156 W
    b.   196 W
    c.   221 W
    d.   313 W
    e.   None of the above

Answer: 156 W

11. A 12:1 step down transformer has an 18 Ω resistive load in the secondary. The equivalent primary resistance due to this load is:

a.   0.125 Ω
b.   1.50 Ω
c.   216 Ω
d.   2.6 kΩ
e.   None of the above

Answer: 2.6 kΩ

12.   A series RLC circuit consists of $R = 330$ Ω, $C = 0.25$ μF, and $L = 500$ mH. The impedance of this circuit at 400 Hz is:

    a.   380 Ω
    b.   470 Ω
    c.   842 Ω
    d.   1.26 kΩ
    e.   None of the above

Answer: 470 Ω

13.   A series RLC circuit consists of $R = 330$ Ω, $C = 0.25$ μF, and $L = 500$ mH. The phase angle between the current and the applied voltage is:

    a. $-45°$
    b. $45°$
    c. $-60°$
    d. $60°$
    e.   None of the above

Answer: $-45°$

14.   The secondary of a transformer has a resistor which is dissipating 1.8 W when a 120 V emf (peak) is applied to the primary. The primary peak current is:

    a.   15 mA
    b.   30 mA
    c.   45 mA
    d.   60 mA
    e.   None of the above

Answer: 30 mA

15.   What is the rms current in an ac circuit where a capacitor of capacitance $C = 1.0 \mu$F is connected across the 120V rms source operating at 60Hz?

    a.   15 mA
    b.   30 mA
    c.   44 mA
    d.   60 mA
    e.   None of the above

Answer: 44 mA

16.   Suppose that a 25.0Ω resistor, 30.0mH inductor and a 12.0μC capacitor are connected in series with each other and that they are connected to a 90.0V rms power source operating at 500Hz. What is the (rms) voltage drop across the capacitor?

    a.   33.1V
    b.   16.5V

c. 66.2V
d. 99.3V
e. None of the above

Answer: 33.1V

17. The secondary of a transformer has a resistor which is dissipating 1.8 W when a 120 V emf (peak) is applied to the primary. If the resistor is 10 Ω, the turns ratio of the transformer (Np/Ns) is:

a. 5:1
b. 10:1
c. 20:1
d. 40:1
e. None of the above

Answer: 20:1

21.0 - PROBLEMS

18. An oscillating LC current has a 120 mH inductor and a 0.33 μF capacitor. The maximum charge on the capacitor is 18 μC. (a) Calculate the resonant frequency of the circuit. (b) Calculate the maximum current through the inductor.

Answer: (a) 800 Hz; (b) 90 mA

19. In the circuit shown, the switch is in position

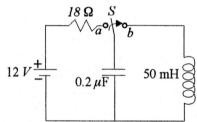

a until the capacitor is fully charged and then moved to position b. (a) Calculate the minimum time (5 time constants) that the switch must be in position a. (b) Calculate the maximum energy stored on the capacitor. (c) Calculate the maximum current through the inductor.

Answer: (a) 18 μs; (b) 14 μJ; (c) 24 mA

20. A series RLC circuit consisting of $R = 180$ Ω, $L = 225$ mH, and $C = 1.5$ μF is connected to a 400 Hz, 140 V emf. (a) Calculate the maximum current in the circuit. (b) Calculate the phase difference between the emf and current.

Answer: (a) 0.40 A; (b) 59°

21. A series RLC circuit consisting of $R = 180$ Ω, $L = 225$ mH, and $C = 1.5$ μF is connected to a 400 Hz, 140 V emf. (a) Calculate the average power dissipated in the resistor. (b) Calculate the power factor of the circuit.

Answer: (a) 14 W; (b) 0.51

22. An ideal transformer steps down from 12 kV, 60 Hz, to 172 V. The average power delivered to a load is 12 kW with a power factor of 0.76. (a) Calculate the turns ratio (Np/Ns). (b) Calculate the rms current in the secondary winding. (c) Calculate the peak current in the primary winding.

Answer: (a) 70; (b) 130 A; (c) 2.6 A

23. A nonideal 120 mH inductor and a 0.33 μF capacitor are in series with a 825 Hz, 1.45 V emf. The phase angle is 80°. (a) Calculate the distributed resistance of the inductor. (b) Calculate the power loss of this LC circuit. (c) Calculate the resonant frequency of this LC circuit.

Answer: (a) 6.6 Ω; (b) 4.8 mW; (c) 800 Hz

24. A nonideal 120 mH inductor and a 0.33 μF capacitor are in series with a 825 Hz, 1.45 V emf. The phase angle is 80°. (a) calculate the maximum energy stored by the inductor. (b) If the frequency is changed to 800 Hz, calculate the maximum energy stored by the inductor.

Answer: (a) 87 μJ; (b) 2.9 mJ

25. A series RLC circuit is driven by a 115 V AC (rms) source. If the maximum voltage drop across each element is the same as the the others sometime during a cycle, (a) calculate this voltage. (b) Calculate the phase angle.

Answer: (a) 163 V; (b) 0

26. A series RLC circuit is driven by a 115 V AC (rms) source. If the maximum voltage drop across the inductor is half that across the resistor, but the maximum voltage drop across the capacitor is twice that across the resistor, (a) calculate the value of R for 230 mA peak currrent. (b) Calculate the phase angle.

Answer: (a) 390 Ω; (b) −56°

27. A series RLC circuit consists of $R = 56$ Ω, $C = 3.3$ μF, $L = 28$ mH, and a 24 V, 400 Hz source. (a) Calculate the rms voltage across R. (b) Calculate the rms voltage across C. (c) Calculate the rms voltage across L.

Answer: (a) 12.6 V; (b) 27.2 V; (c) 15.9 V

28. A 64 V AC (rms) source drives the primary

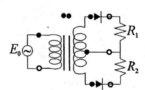

of an ideal 3:1 transformer with a center tapped secondary and two ideal diodes, as shown. If $R_1 = 120$ Ω and $R_2 = 150$ Ω, (a) calculate the peak current through R_1 and R_2. (b) Calculate the average power dissipated in R_1 and R_2.

Answer: (a) 126 mA, 100 mA; (b) 476 mW, 375 mW

29. A generator supplies 120 V (peak) at 1000 Hz and 1.6 A (peak) with a power factor of 0.67. (a) Calculate the resistance of the load. (b) If $C = 20$ μF, calculate the inductance of the load.

Answer: (a) 50 Ω; (b) 10 mH

30. A variable inductor is used with 115 V AC, 60 Hz line to dim a 250 W light bulb from 250 W to 50 W. (a) Calculate the maximum value the inductor must have. (b) Calculate the power factor of the load when fully dimmed (assume R does not change with power). (c) Calculate the power factor under full 250 W.

Answer: (a) 281 mH; (b) 0.45; (c) 1.0

31. An RLC circuit consists of $E_0 = 60$ V (peak), 400 Hz, $R = 18$ Ω, and $L = 390$ mH. (a) Calculate the value of C for maximum power dissipation in the resistor. (b) Calculate this maximum power. (c) Calculate the value of C for minimum power dissipation in the resistor. (d) Calculate this minimum power.

Answer: (a) 0.41 μF; (b)100 W; (c) 0; (d) 1.8 W

32. A 60mH inductor with 7.0Ω resistance is connected in series to a $300\mu F$ capacitor and a 60Hz, 55V (rms) source. (a) What is the rms current? (b) What is the phase angle? (c) How much power is dissipated?

Answer: (a) 3.6A (b); 63^0; (c) 89 W

33. If 50kW is to be transmitted over two 0.100Ω lines, estimate how much power is saved if the voltage is stepped up from 120V to 1200V and then down again, rather then transmitting as 120V. Assume that the transformers are each 99% efficient.

Answer: 33.4kW

34. A variable air capacitor with a range of 20 pF to 200 pF is in series with an inductor to tune the AM radio band from 540 kHz to 1.60 MHz. Calculate the optimum value of fixed inductance for this LC circuit.

Answer: 0.47 mH

CHAPTER 22

22.0 - MULTIPLE CHOICE QUESTIONS

1. The average wavelength of light from a 100 W light bulb is 550 nm. The number of photons emitted per second is:

    a. 1.4×10^{20}
    b. 2.8×10^{20}
    c. 4.5×10^{20}
    d. 6.2×10^{20}
    e.   None of the above

    Answer: 2.8×10^{20}

2. An electron ($m = 9.1 \times 10^{-31}$ kg) is accelerated through a potential of 120 volts. The electron's speed is:

    a. 5.8×10^5 m/s
    b. 9.1×10^5 m/s
    c. 6.5×10^6 m/s
    d. 7.2×10^6 m/s
    e.   None of the above

    Answer: 6.5×10^6 m/s

3. In a TV picture tube, electrons are accelerated through a 12 kilovolt potential. The wavelength of the x-rays emitted when the electron strikes the screen is:

    a.   0.10 nm
    b.   0.20 nm
    c.   0.50 nm
    d.   1.0 nm
    e.   None of the above

    Answer: 0.10 nm

4. The number of photons per second emitted by a 100 kW AM station operating on 1250 Hz is:

    a. 1.9×10^{18}
    b. 2.4×10^{22}
    c. 3.6×10^{28}
    d. 1.2×10^{32}
    e.   None of the above

    Answer: 1.2×10^{32}

5. If the eye can respond to as few as 300 photons per second of yellow light (600 nm) and if the ear has an effective area of 1.0 mm^2, the ratio of the threshold of sight to the threshold of hearing is:

    a.   greater than one
    b.   one
    c.   less than one
    d.   can not be determined from data given

    Answer: one

152

6. The electric field of a radio wave is 3.0 V/m. The corresponding magnetic field density for a TEM wave is:

   a. 1×10^{-8} T
   b. 3×10^{-8} T
   c. 1×10^{-8} gauss
   d. 3×10^{-8} gauss
   e. None of the above

   Answer: 1×10^{-8} T

7. The electric field of a radio wave is 3.0 V/m. The irradiance of the radio wave is:

   a. 4.4×10^{-3} W/m^2
   b. 8.8×10^{-3} W/m^2
   c. 1.2×10^{-2} W/m^2
   d. 2.4×10^{-2} W/m^2
   e. None of the above

   Answer: 1.2×10^{-2} W/m^2

8. When particles in atomic nuclei change energy levels they emit γ-rays. The wavelength of γ-rays emitted from nuclear levels 2.22 MeV apart is:

   a. 0.056 nm
   b. 0.090 nm
   c. 0.90 nm
   d. 0.56 pm
   e. None of the above

   Answer: 0.56 pm

9. A wavenumber used in IR spectroscopy is $k/2\pi$ where k is the propagation number. The wavelength of 100 wavenumber radiation is:

   a. $1/2\pi \times 10^5$ nm
   b. 100 μm
   c. 100π μm
   d. 200π μm
   e. None of the above

   Answer: 100 μm

10. The FM antenna wire on the back of your hi-fi receiver is two $\frac{1}{4} \lambda$ in length sections. If the center of the FM band is used, the length of a section should be:

    a. 25 inches
    b. 28 inches
    c. 30 inches
    d. 39 inches
    e. None of the above

    Answer: 30 in

11. A TEM wave has an irradiance of 108 mW/m^2. The associate peak electric field is:

    a. 2.4 V/m

153

b.   6.2 V/m
c.   9.0 V/m
d.   13 V/m
e.   None of the above

Answer: 9.0 V/m

12.   A TEM wave has an irradiance of 108 mW/m^2. The associated peak magnetic field is:

a. 3×10^{-6} T
b. 3×10^{-8} T
c. 6×10^{-8} T
d.   10.8 T
e.   None of the above

Answer: 3×10^{-8} T

13.   The electric field of a sinusoidal 1 MHz TEM wave goes to zero for the first time after emission at which of the following times:

a. $0.5\ \mu s$
b. $1.0\ \mu s$
c. $2.0\ \mu s$
d. $5.0\ \mu s$
e.   None of the above

Answer: $0.5\ \mu s$

14.   What is the wavelength of a 60Hz electromagnetic wave?

a.   500 m
b.   50,000 m
c.   500,000 m
d.   5,000,000 m
e.   None of the above

Answer: 5,000,000 m

15.   Radiation form the sun reaches earth (above the atomsphere) at a rate of about 1350 W/m^2.Assuming that this is a single electromagnetic wave, what is the average strength of the electric field?

a. 1.01×10^3V/m
b. 2.02×10^5V/m
c. 3.14×10^{-6}V/m
d. 1.00×10^{14}V/m
e.   None of the above

Answer: 1.01×10^3V/m

16.   If a microwave oven operates at 2.45 GHz, which of the following number of complete wavelengths would span a 15 inch long space:

a.   1/2
b.   1
c.   2
d.   3
e.   None of the above

154

17. A light beam of 6.25 W/m^2 irradiance impinges on a perfectly absorbing planar surface of 10 cm^2 area. The amount of energy absorbed in 4 minutes is:

   a.   1.5 J
   b.   3.0 J
   c.   4.5 J
   d.   6.0 J
   e.   None of the above

Answer: 1.5 J

22.0 - PROBLEMS

18. A 1.0 mW He-Ne laser with a circular beam diameter of 2.5 mm operates at 632.8 nm. (a) Calculate the photon flux. (b) Calculate the number of photons in a 50 ns pulse. (c) Calculate energy density in the pulse.

Answer: (a) 6.5×10^{16} photons/cm^2-s; (b) 1.6×10^8; (c) 6.8×10^{-13} J/cm^3

19. The maximum electric field at 8.0 m from a point source of light has a value of 0.25 v/cm. (a) Calculate the power output of the light source. (b) Calculate the intensity of the light source. (c) Calculate the maximum magnetic field at 4.0 m.

Answer: (a) 668 W; (b) 0.830 W/m^2; (c) 1.67×10^{-7} T

20. A Nd: glass laser provides 5×10^{12} W of power in the IR at 0.26 μm in 10 ns pulses. (a) Calculate the energy in the pulse. (b) Calculate the number of photons in the pulse.

Answer: (a) 5.0×10^4 J; (b) 6.54×10^{22}

21. A 5.0 mW He-Ne laser (632.8 nm) with a 2.5 mm circular beam and a beam divergence given by $\phi = 1.27\lambda/D$ where D is the exit beam diameter, illuminates a screen 100 m away. (a) Calculate the beam intensity on the screen. (b) Calculate the corresponding beam intensity on the wall for a UV laser (193 nm) (Argon excimer laser).

Answer: (a) 53 mW/cm^2; (b) 420 mW/cm^2

22. Radiation force exerted by a light source is given by Newton's Second Law where the momentum, p, is given as $p = U/c$ (total absorption) or $p = 2U/c$ (total reflection) where U is the energy absorbed or reflected. (a) Calculate the radiation force of a 10^{12} W Nd: glass laser with 10 ns pulses for total reflection. (b) Calculate the radiation force in pounds for a 75% reflective surface.

Answer: (a) 6.67×10^3 N; (b) 1.31×10^3 lb

23. Light with an intensity of 25 W/cm^2 strikes a 1.0 inch diameter mirror and is totally reflected. (a) Calculate the radiation pressure on the mirror. (b) Calculate the total radiation force on the mirror in ounces.

Answer: (a) 1.67×10^{-3} N/m^2; (b) 3.04×10^{-6} oz

24. Suppose sunlight in space has an intensity of 1500 W/cm^2. A 1000 kg spaceship uses a 100 m × 100 m reflective (Al coated) Mylar sail for propulsion. (a) Calculate the force exerted by sunlight normal to the sail. (b) Calculate the speed (in mph) the spaceship obtains after using the sail 10 days.

Answer: (a) 0.10 N (b) 193 mi/h

25. The beam from a 1.0 W He-Ne laser (632.8 nm) is focused to a 2λ diameter spot. (a) Calculate the maximum electric field. (b) Calculate the maximum magnetic field (in gauss).

Answer: (a) 2.45×10^7 V/m; (b) 815×10^{-4} T

26. A 20 W Argon ion laser (514.5 nm) with a 2.5 mm effective circular beam diameter is used to illuminate the moon's surface (3.74×10^8 m away). (a) Calculate the beam divergence of this laser. (b) Calculate the diameter of the illuminated area on the moon. (c) Calculate the intensity of the laser radiation on the moon.

Answer: (a) 2.62×10^{-4} rad; (b) 97.8 km; (c) 2.66×10^{-9} W/m^2

27. A 1.0 kW CO_2 laser (10.6 μm) has a circular beam diameter of 0.5 cm. It is used to cut firebrick ($\rho = 5.6$ g/cm^3, $c = 0.18$ cal/g K) which sublimes at 2400 K. (a) Calculate the time for the beam to cut a hole through 1.0 inch firebrick if the beam is completely absorbed (assume uniform volumetric heating). (b) Calculate the maximum electric field in the beam. (c) Calculate the maximum magnetic field density in the beam.

Answer: (a) 17.7 s; (b) 9.79×10^4 V/m; (c) 3.26×10^{-4} T

28. As you walk down a pier you note that the white mooring light atop a mast gets twice as "bright" as you get 75 feet closer. (a) Calculate your original distance from the light. (b) If the original intensity was 0.26 mW/m^2 and the light is 8% efficient in converting electrical energy to light, calculate the wattage of the light bulb.

Answer: (a) 256 ft; (b) 250 W

29. Sunlight strikes normal to earth's surface with an intensity of 1.4 kW/m^2. (a) Calculate the maximum electric field and associated magnetic field of sunlight. (b) Assuming the earth behaves as a completely absorbing, flat disc normal to the sunlight with a diameter equal to 3/4 earth's diameter (1.27×10^7 m), calculate the solar radiation force ($p = U/c$).

Answer: (a) 1.03×10^3 V/m, 3.42×10^{-6} T ; (b) 3.32×10^8 N

30. A 10 kW CO_2 laser with a perfectly collimated 2.0 cm diameter beam is used to accelerate a 5 g reflective projectile of the same diameter. (a) Calculate the radiation pressure for reflection normal to the projectile base ($p = 2U/c$). (b) Calculate the acceleration of the projectile. (c) Calculate the time required to accelerate the projectile to 1000 fps.

Answer: (a) 0.212 N/m^2; (b) 1.33×10^{-2} m/s^2; (c) 6 hr, 21 min

31. An 18 W Argon ion laser (514.5 nm) with a 2.5 mm beam diameter is used to levitate a circular 12 μg disc of the same diameter. (a) Calculate the radiation intensity near the laser. (b) Calculate the radiation intensity required to levitate the disc for complete reflection ($p = 2U/c$). (c) Calculate the height the disc will levitate above the laser due to beam divergence ($\phi = 1.27\lambda/D$).

Answer: (a) 3.67×10^6 W/m^2; (b) 3.59×10^6 W/m$^{2;}$ (c) 4.8 cm

32. An FM radio station transmits at 100MHz. (a) What is the wavelength? (b) What is the value of the capacitance of the tuning circuit if the the inductance is 0.4μH?

Answer: (a) 3.0m; (b) 6.3pF

33. Suppose a 5kW radio station emits electromagnetic waves uniformly in all directions. How much energy per second crosses a 1.0m^2 area 100m from the transmitting antenna?

Answer: 0.40 W/m^2

34. A 10 m high vertical antenna radiates 1000 W of power in a cylindrical wave which increases in height by 10^{-3} radians (like beam divergence). (a) Calculate the maximum height (in feet) that an aircraft 100 miles

away can be and still receive the signal. (b) Calculate the intensity of the signal if the aircraft is 100 miles away at an altitude of 500 feet.

Answer: (a) 561 ft; (b) 5.79 μW/m^2

CHAPTER 23

1. A pinhole camera has 20 cm between the pinhole and the image at the back of the camera.   If the image is 6.0 cm high for a tree 50 m away, the height of the tree is:

    a.   10 m
    b.   15 m
    c.   20 m
    d.   25 m
    e.   None of the above

    Answer: 15 m

2. A pinhole camera has a 4.0 cm high image of a flag pole. Moving back 9.0 m with the camera reduces the image to 3.0 cm. The original distance to the flag pole was:

    a.   20 m
    b.   21 m
    c.   24 m
    d.   27 m
    e.   None of the above

    Answer: 27 m

3. The critical angle for internal reflection for a diamond ($n = 2.417$) is about:

    a.   18°
    b.   24°
    c.   30°
    d.   36°
    e.   None of the above

    Answer: 24°

4. A beam of light enters a glass plate at an angle of incidence of 25.0° resulting in an angle of tr Ansmission of 15.5°. The index of refraction of the glass is:

    a.   1.54
    b.   1.56
    c.   1.58
    d.   1.60
    e.   None of the above

    Answer: 1.58

5. Two perfectly in-phase light beams from a He-Ne laser (632.8 nm) travel 1 m through air and are rejoined in-phase. If one of the beams has a 1 mm thick glass slide ($n = 1.52$) interposed in its path normal to the beam, the phase difference (in degrees) when they are rejoined is:

    a. 1×10^2
    b. 6×10^3
    c. 5×10^4
    d. 3×10^5

e.   None of the above

Answer: 3×10^5

6.   The optical path length of a light beam is nd where n is the refractive index and d is the physical distance. A light beam passes through 2.0 in. of thick glass ($n = 1.525$) then through 12 in. of water and finally through 0.60 in. of polystyrene ($n = 1.590$). The optical path length is:

    a.   14 in
    b.   16 in
    c.   20 in
    d.   24 in
    e.   None of the above

Answer: 20 in

7.   The reflectance, R, of non-conductive materials at normal incidence can be written $R = [(n - 1)/(n + 1)]^2$. The reflectance of crown glass ($n = 1.52$) is:

    a.   4.3%
    b.   4.5%
    c.   4.6%
    d.   4.8%
    e.   None of the above

Answer: 4.3%

8.   A silvered mirror 90° corner reflector, as shown, has light with an angle of incidence of 30° on one face. The angle of incidence of the reflected ray on the other face is:

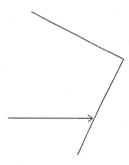

    a.   15°
    b.   30°
    c.   45°
    d.   60°
    e.   None of the above

Answer: 60°

9.   A silvered mirror 90° corner reflector, as shown, has light with an angle of incidence of 30° on one face. The angle between the incident and reflected rays of the corner reflector is:

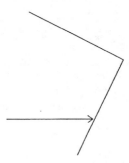

a.   45°
b.   60°
c.   120°
d.   180°
e.   None of the above

Answer: 180°

10.   Light is incident upon a 4.6 mm diameter diamond sphere, as shown ($n = 2.417$). The distance the refracted ray passes from the center of the sphere is:

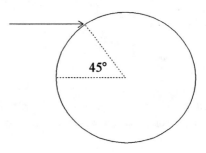

a.   2.5 mm
b.   0.5 mm
c.   0.7 mm
d.   0.9 mm
e.   None of the above

Answer: 0.7 mm

11.   A fiber optic cable of crown glass ($n = 1.52$) has a cladding sheath of special material ($n = 1.32$), as shown. The critical angle for light transmission is:

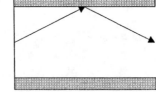

a.   58°
b.   60°
c.   62°
d.   68°
e.   None of the above

160

Answer: 60°

12. Cerenkov radiation is emitted by an electron traveling faster than the speed of light in a medium as it slows down. The minimum speed for Cerenkov radiation in rutile ($n = 2.907$) is about:

    a. 1.0×10^8 m/s
    b. 1.2×10^8 m/s
    c. 1.8×10^8 m/s
    d. 2.4×10^8 m/s
    e.   None of the above

Answer: 1.0×10^8 m/s

13. A scuba diver 10 m under water looks at what angle (with respect to the horizontal) in order to see the Moon 30° above the horizon?

    a.   22°
    b.   30°
    c.   50°
    d.   60°
    e.   None of the above

Answer: 50°

14. An object is 2 ft in front of you and you are 4 ft in front of a plane mirror. What distance is the image from you?

    a.   3 ft
    b.   4 ft
    c.   5 ft
    d.   6 ft
    e.   None of the above

Answer: 6 ft

15. Light strikes a flat slab of glass at an incident angle of 60^0. If the index of refraction of the glass is 1.50 at what angle does the beam emerge from the slab?

    a. 60^0
    b. 90^0
    c. 45^0
    d. 30^0
    e.   None of the above

Answer: 60^0

16. A flashlight beam strikes the surface of a pane of glass (n = 1.50) at a 45^0 angle. What is the angle of refraction?

    a. 60^0
    b. 15^0
    c. 45^0
    d. 28^0
    e.   None of the above

17.   A 48 cm wide mirror has an object initially 3.0 m directly in front of it, as shown. An observer is 3.0 m to the left of the object initially. How close must the object be to the mirror for the observer to first see the image?

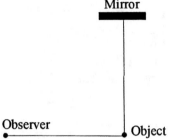

a.   20 cm
b.   26 cm
c.   38 cm
d.   54 cm
e.   None of the above

Answer: 26 cm

23.0 - PROBLEMS

18.   The optical path length, Δ, is given as $\Delta = nd$ where n is the refractive index and d is the actual distance. Two light beams travel 10.0 cm, one through air and the other through air and 0.500 cm of Zircon ($n = 1.923$). (a) Calculate the optical path difference of the two beams. (b) If, instead, the optical path difference was measured to be 7.085 mm for 0.500 cm of material, what material might this be?
                                                          Answer: (a) 4.62 mm; (b) diamond

19.   A helium point light source (587.6 nm) passes light through a 5.00 mm thick dense flint glass ($n = 1.72$) at an angle of incidence of 45°. (a) Calculate the angle of refraction. (b) Calculate the off-set of the refracted ray as it exits relative to the incident ray's path extended.
                                                          Answer: (a) 24.3°; (b) 1.94 mm

20.   Two small point beams of light, one red (656.3 nm) and the other blue (486.1 nm) are incident at 48° on flint glass with indices of refraction of 1.713 and 1.738, respectively. (a) Calculate the angle between the refracted beams. (b) If the glass is 7.50 mm thick and silvered on the bottom side, calculate the distance between the entrance and exit points of the blue light.
                                                          Answer: (a) 0.40°; (b) 7.09 mm

21.   A square tank 17.0 cm on a side and 17.0 cm

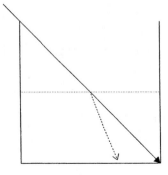

162

high is viewed over one edge, as shown. With the tank empty the bottom-edge joint can just be seen. The tank is then filled halfway with an unknown fluid and the line of vision is 4.40 cm back from the joint. (a) Calculate the index of refraction of the fluid. (b) Identify the possible fluid involved.

Answer: (a) 1.63; (b) CS_2

22. A hollow pipe 75.0 cm long has two 5.00 mm thick lanthanum flint glass plates attached at either end. (a) Calculate the optical path length with air in the pipe. (b) Calculate the optical path length with water in the pipe. (c) Calculate the optical path length with a 50/50 mixture of C_2H_5OH and C_6H_6 in the pipe.

Answer: (a) 76.8 cm; (b) 101.8 cm; (c) 109.1 cm

23. A Fabry-Perot optical cavity consists essentially

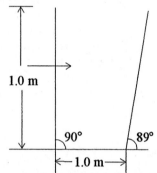

of two parallel plane mirrors facing each other and reflecting a light beam back and forth. If a laser light beam enters through a small hole halfway up, as shown; (a) Calculate the number of times the beam strikes the entrance mirror. (b) Calculate the distance between the exiting beam and the top of the mirror that it first misses.

Answer: (a) 2; (b) 4.8 cm

24. A small laser light beam strikes a zircon

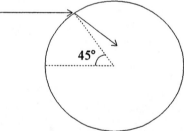

sphere ($n = 1.923$), as shown. (a) Calculate the angle the refracted beam makes with the original path extended. (b) Calculate the angle the exiting beam makes with the original path extended.

Answer: (a) 23.4°; (b) 45°

25. The acceptance angle, θ_A, for fiber optics

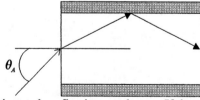

is the maximum input angle for total internal reflection, as shown. If the core has an index of refraction of 1.58 and the cladding 1.46; (a) Calculate the acceptance angle. If the reflection, R, is given as

$R = [(n - 1)/(n + 1)]^2$ for normal incidence; (b) Calculate the percent of the light reflected at normal incidence of input light.

Answer: (a) 37.2°; (b) 5%

26. A penny at the bottom of a fish tank filled with 16 in. of water is viewed at an angle of incidence at the surface of 60°. (a) Calculate the apparent depth of the penny. (b) If viewed at an angle of incidence of 43° through 16 in. of CS_2, what is the apparent depth.

Answer: (a) 7.9 in; (b) 7.9 in

27. A person whose eyes are 1.48m above the floor stands 2.40m in front of a vertical plane mirror whose bottom edge is 40cm above the floor. What is the horizontal distance to the base of the wall supporting the mirror of the nearest point on the floor that can be seen in the mirror?

Answer: 89cm

28. A beam of light is emitted 8.0cm beneath the surface of a liquid and strikes the surface 7.0cm from the point directly above the source. If the total internal reflection occurs, what can you say about the index of refraction of the liquid?

Answer: $n \geq 1.52$

29. An optical prism system consists of an

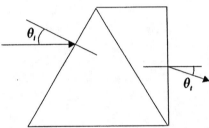

equilateral triangle prism of crown glass ($n = 1.52$) and a 30-60 right triangle prism of dense flint glass, as shown. Calculate the angle, θ_t, of the transmitted ray, if the angle of incidence, θ_i, is 30°.

Answer: 9.1°

30. A 0.120 mm thick quartz cover glass has

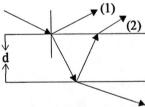

finely focused Ar-ion laser light (514.5 nm) incident at 81.5° from the vertical. The beam is reflected and transmitted from both surfaces, as shown. (a) Calculate the optical path difference for rays (1) and (2). (b) Calculate the number of wavelengths by which rays (1) and (2) differ.

Answer: (a) 0.257 mm (b) 500

31. Light is incident on a 45.0° prism, as shown.

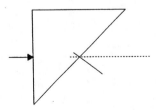

(a) Calculate the angle that the transmitted ray makes with the extended path of the incident ray if $n = 1.385$. (b) Calculate this angle for $n = 1.4148$. (c) Calculate this angle for $n = 1.485$.

Answer: (a) 33.3°; (b) 45°(c) 90°

32. A pilot in an aircraft flying at 120 mi/h, 1000 ft above the water observes a light signal from a submersible, 500 ft below the water, dead ahead and at an angle of 25° below the horizontal. (a) Calculate the time until the aircraft is over the submersible. (b) Calculate the time it took the light signal, originally, to travel from the submersible to the aircraft.

Answer: (a) 14.8 s; (b) 3.34 μs

33. A Dove prism (reverses right and left) is

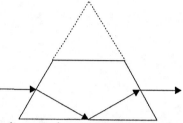

truncated from an equilateral triangle prism, as shown. (a) Calculate the critical angle for internal reflection for a crown glass ($n = 1.52$) prism. (b) Calculate the angle of incidence of the ray shown on the bottom face of the prism.

Answer: (a) 41.1°; (b) 79.2°

34. A crown glass ($n = 1.52$) 30-60 prism has light incident

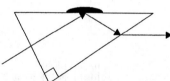

normal to the short leg, as shown. A drop of liquid is placed on the hypotenuse causing internal reflection. (a) Calculate the maximum index of refraction the liquid can have. (b) Calculate the angle between the entering and exiting rays for internal reflection.

Answer: (a) 1.316; (b) 40°

CHAPTER 24

24.0 - MULTIPLE CHOICE QUESTIONS

1.   The focal length of a crown glass ($n = 1.52$) plano-convex lens of 10 cm radius is:

   a.   0.10 cm
   b.   10 cm
   c.   19 cm
   d. ∞
   e.   None of the above

                                              Answer: 19 cm

2.   The focal length of a crown glass ($n = 1.52$) biconvex lens of radii 4.0 cm and 6.0 cm is:

   a.   2.4 cm
   b.   4.6 cm
   c.   8.2 cm
   d.   23 cm
   e.   None of the above

                                              Answer: 4.6 cm

3.   The focal length of a crown glass ($n = 1.52$) biconcave lens of radii 4.0 cm and 6.0 cm is:

   a. -2.4 cm
   b. -4.6 cm
   c.   2.4 cm
   d. -23 cm
   e.   None of the above

                                              Answer: -4.6 cm

4.   The image distance of a meniscus convex lens (convex-concave) for an object 3.0 f away from the lens is:

   a.   1.5 f
   b.   2.0 f
   c.   2.5 f
   d.   3.0 f
   e.   None of the above

                                              Answer: 1.5 f

5.   The focal length of a positive lens with object and image distances of 24 cm and 48 cm, respectively, is:

   a.   8 cm
   b.   12 cm
   c.   15 cm
   d.   16 cm
   e.   None of the above

                                              Answer: 16 cm

6.   A crown glass ($n = 1.52$) biconvex lens has a focal length of 23 cm in air. Its focal length in water is:

   a.   39 cm
   b.   48 cm
   c.   64 cm
   d.   82 cm

e.   None of the above

Answer: None of the above

7.   A 12 cm tall wine glass is 50 cm from a positive lens of focal length 25 cm. The image height is:

a.   6 cm
b.   12 cm
c.   18 cm
d.   24 cm
e.   None of the above

Answer: 12 cm

8.   The equivalent focal length of lenses in contact add like resistors in parallel. A 78 cm focal length meniscus convex lens and a 48 cm focal length biconvex lens are fused together to form a compound lens. The focal length of the compound lens is:

a.   30 cm
b.   40 cm
c.   50 cm
d.   60 cm
e.   None of the above

Answer: 30 cm

9.   An 18 cm radius concave spherical mirror has a 6.0 cm high object 6.0 cm away. The image height is:

a.   2 cm
b.   6 cm
c.   12 cm
d.   18 cm
e.   None of the above

Answer: 18 cm

10.   A plano-convex dense flint glass ($n = 1.66$) lens has a power of 3.0 D (a diopter, D, is the reciprocal of the focal length in meters). The radius of convex curvature is:

a.   11 cm
b.   18 cm
c.   22 cm
d.   30 cm
e.   None of the above

Answer: 22 cm

11.   A 1.50cm high object is placed 20.0cm from a concave mirror whose radius of curvature is 30.0cm. What is the size of the image?

a.   4.5 cm
b.   -5.4 cm
c.   -4.5 cm
d.   5.4 cm
e.   None of the above

Answer: -4.5 cm

12.   What is the position of the image of a large 22.4cm high object placed 1.50m from a $+50.0$mm focal length camera lens?

a. 55.7mm
b. 51.7mm
c. 49.7mm
d. 30.7mm
e. None of the above

Answer: 51.7m

13. An equiconcave ($|R_1| = |R_2|$) lens of flint glass ($n = 1.80$) has a power of -8.0 D. The radii of curvature must be:

a. 20 cm
b. 25 cm
c. 40 cm
d. 60 cm
e. None of the above

Answer: 20 cm

14. A 40 cm radius shaving mirror is positioned to double the face image. The distance the face is from the mirror is:

a. 10 cm
b. 16 cm
c. 24 cm
d. 30 cm
e. None of the above

Answer: 10 cm

15. A 2.4 cm diameter collimated light beam enters a lens and diverges in a cone with apex angle of 73.7°. The focal length of the lens is:

a. -1.2 cm
b. -1.6 cm
c. -2.0 cm
d. -2.4 cm
e. None of the above

Answer: -1.6 cm

16. A crown glass ($n = 1.52$) lens of radii $R_1 = 12$ cm and $R_2 = -22$ cm has a power of:

a. 1.8 D
b. 2.0 D
c. 2.4 D
d. 3.0 D
e. None of the above

Answer: None of the above

17. A crown glass ($n = 1.52$) meniscus concave lens of radii 48 cm and 25 cm is positioned horizontally with the concave side up. If filled with benezene ($n = 1.50$), the focal length of this combination would be:

a. 22 cm
b. 28 cm
c. 33 cm
d. 49 cm
e. None of the above

Answer: 49 cm

168

18. A beam of collimated light $r\sqrt{2}$ in diameter is incident upon a glass sphere of radius, r, and is brought to focus on the back surface. (a) Calculate the index of refraction of the glass. (b) Calculate the cone apex angle of the exiting beam.

    Answer: (a) 1.848; (b) 90°

19. When an object is placed 10 cm in front of a positive lens, the image is 4 times as far away as when the object is at 10 m. (a) Calculate the focal length of the lens. (b) Calculate the magnification of the lens.

    Answer: (a) 7.6 cm; (b) 3.3

20. A crown glass ($n = 1.52$) biconcave lens of radii 20.0 cm and 30.0 cm has an object placed 30.0 cm in front of the lens. (a) Calculate the focal length of the lens. (b) Calculate the image position. (c) Calculate the lens magnification. (d) Is the image erect or inverted?

    Answer: (a) −23.1 cm; (b) −13.0 cm; (c) −0.43; (d) Erect

21. A compound lens system consists of two biconvex lenses. The first lens has a focal length of 10 cm, the second lens of 20 cm. The lenses are 60 cm apart. An object is placed 15 cm in front of the first lens. (a) Calculate the image distance of the first lens. (b) Calculate the image distance of the second lens. (c) Calculate the magnification of the compound lens. (d) Is the final image erect or inverted?

    Answer: (a) 30 cm; (b) 60 cm; (c) 4; (d) Erect

22. A 30.0 cm concave spherical mirror is used to project an image on a screen 4.00 m away. (a) Calculate the object distance from the mirror. (b) Calculate the magnification of the image. (c) Is the image erect or inverted?

    Answer: (a) 15.6 cm; (b) 25.7; (c) Inverted

23. Two biconvex lenses are placed in contact to form a compound lens. The first lens is made of crown glass ($n = 1.52$) with radii 9.00 cm and 12.0 cm. The second lens is made of flint glass ($n = 1.66$) with radii 12 cm and 20 cm. (a) Calculate the powers (in diopters) of the individual lenses. (b) Calculate the power of the compound lens. (c) Calculate the focal lengths of the individual lenses. (d) Calculate the focal length of the compound lens.

    Answer: (a) 10.1 D, 8.80 D; (b) 18.9 D; (c) 9.90 cm, 11.4 cm; (d) 5.3 cm

24. A projector slide is 4.0 cm tall and is to be projected upon a screen 3.0 m away to form an image 1.0 m tall. (a) Calculate the distance between the slide and the lens. (b) Calculate the focal length of the lens. (c) Is the image real or virtual? (d) Is the image erect or inverted?

    Answer: (a) 12 cm; (b) 11.5 cm; (c) Real; (d) inverted

25. An object is placed 12 cm in front of a 30 cm radius convex mirror. (a) Calculate the focal length of the mirror. (b) Calculate the image position. (c) Calculate the magnification.

    Answer: (a) −15 cm; (b) −6.7 cm; (c) 0.56

26. An object is placed 12 cm in front of a lens of focal length 6.0 cm. A second lens of focal length −15 cm is placed 4.0 cm behind the first lens. (a) Calculate the focal length of the compound lens $(1/f_c = 1/f_1 + 1/f_2 - d/f_1 f_2)$. (b) Calculate the final image position from the second lens. (c) Calculate the magnification of the compound lens.

    Answer: (a) 6.92 cm; (b) 17.1 cm; (c) −2.14

27. A telephoto lens consists of a 5.0 cm focal length biconvex lens 3.0 cm away from a −2.5 cm focal length biconvex lens. (a) Calculate the focal length of the lens system. (b) Calculate the final image position for a parallel incident light source. (c) If the photo surface is the image plane, calculate the overall length of the camera (first lens to image plane).

28. Three lenses of focal lengths $f_1 = 5.0$ cm, $f_2 = 10$ cm, and $f_3 = 20$ cm are placed in contact to form a compound lens. Calculate the focal length of the compound lens.

Answer: 3.0 cm

29. A simple camera consists of a positive lens of 5.00 cm focal length. (a) How far from a 2.00 m tall family scene must you be to capture it on 25 mm film? (b) Calculate the distance from the lens to the film (image plane).

Answer: (a) 4.05 m; (b) 5.06 cm

30. An equiconvex flint glass lens ($n = 1.66$) is to have a power of 2.0 D. (a) Calculate the radii of curvature. (b) The lens is immersed in water, calculate the power of the lens under water. (c) Calculate the radii of curvature to make this lens have 2.0 D power under water.

Answer: (a) 66 cm; (b) 1.0 D; (c) 33 cm

31. A positive lens of 18 cm focal length is to be placed between an object and screen 96 cm apart. (a) Calculate the two positions from the object at which the lens should be placed to form a real image. (b) Calculate the corresponding magnification.

Answer: (a) 24 cm, 72 cm; (b) 3, 1/3

32. To measure the focal length of a diverging lens, a converging lens is placed in contact with it. The sun rays are focused by this combination at a point 28.5cm behind the lenses. If the focal length of a converging lens is 16.0cm, what is the focal length of a diverging lens?

Answer: -36.5cm

33. A lucite planeconvex lens has one flat surface and the other has radius of curvature R $= -18.4$cm. What is the focal length? (The index of refraction of lucite is 1.51.)

Answer: (a) 72 cm

34. A beam expander-collimator is to be constructed to expand a 2.00 mm diameter laser beam into a 2.00 cm diameter laser beam of collimated light. The first lens is a flint glass ($n = 1.80$) equiconvex lens of 2.00 cm radii. (a) Calculate the focal length of the second equiconvex lens. (b) If the second lens is also flint glass equiconvex, calculate the lens radii. (c) Calculate the distance between lenses. (d) Calculate the focal length of the two lens system.

Answer: (a) 12.5 cm; (b) 20 cm; (c) 13.8 cm; (d) ∞

CHAPTER 25

25.0 - MULTIPLE CHOICE QUESTIONS

1. 0.30 W/m² unpolarized light has an electric field of:

   a. 0.30 V/m
   b. 1.2 V/m
   c. 6.0 V/m
   d. 15 V/m
   e. None of the above

   Answer: 15 V/m

2. Unpolarized light is incident upon two ideal linear polarizers. If 25% of the light is transmitted, the angle between the axes of the polarizers is:

   a. 30°
   b. 45°
   c. 60°
   d. 75°
   e. None of the above

   Answer: 45°

3. Unpolarized light is incident upon three ideal linear polarizers with the final two set 45° to the right of the one ahead. The fraction of the light transmitted is:

   a. 0
   b. 1/8
   c. 1/4
   d. 1/2
   e. None of the above

   Answer: 1/8

4. The angle of incidence for the polarization of light incident on plate glass with an index of refraction of 1.58 is:

   a. 48°
   b. 58°
   c. 62°
   d. 72°
   e. None of the above

   Answer: 58°

5. The distance of the second maxima of 632.8 nm light from the axis of the incident light for a 0.12 mm slit separation and a screen 115 cm away is:

   a. 8 mm
   b. 10 mm
   c. 12 mm
   d. 18 mm
   e. None of the above

   Answer: 12 mm

171

6. Monochromatic light is incident upon two slits 0.180 mm apart. The resulting interference pattern is observed on a screen 1.65 m away. If the spacing between minima is 5.00 mm, the wavelength of the light is:

    a.   546 nm
    b.   582 nm
    c.   633 nm
    d.   652 nm
    e.   None of the above

                                           Answer: 546 nm

7. A single slit, 3.0×10^{-3} mm wide, is illuminated by 632.8 nm light. The second minima occurs at an angle of:

    a.   15°
    b.   20°
    c.   25°
    d.   30°
    e.   None of the above

                                           Answer: 25°

8. A small circular aperture gives a 7.0 cm diameter dark ring around the central maximum on a screen 27 cm away when illuminated by 632.8 nm light. The diameter of the aperture is:

    a.   1.2 μm
    b.   2.4 μm
    c.   4.8 μm
    d.   6.0 μm
    e.   None of the above

                                       Answer: 6.0 μm

9. A 0.10 mm wide slit is illuminated by 589 nm light. A diffraction pattern is observed on a screen 2.0 m away. The spacing between the two minima on either side of the central maximum is:

    a.   2.4 cm
    b.   3.2 cm
    c.   3.6 cm
    d.   4.2 cm
    e.   None of the above

                                       Answer: 2.4 cm

10. The critical angle for internal reflection is 42° for a material. The Brewster angle is:

    a.   42°
    b.   48°
    c.   52 °
    d.   56°
    e.   None of the above

                                           Answer: 56°

11. Young's Experiment with an Argon laser (488 nm) uses 1.0 mm slit separation and a screen 5.1 m away. The spacing between bright fringes is:

    a.   1.9 mm
    b.   2.5 mm

c. 3.0 mm
d. 3.3 mm
e. None of the above

Answer: 2.5 mm

12. Using the data of the previous question, what would be the spacing if the experiment was conducted under water ($n = 4/3$)?

   a. 1.9 mm
   b. 2.5 mm
   c. 3.0 mm
   d. 3.3 mm
   e. None of the above

Answer: 1.9 mm

13. 632.8 nm light is incident upon a narrow slit. The angle between the first minimum on one side and the second minimum on the other side is 3.6°. The slit width is?

   a. 10 μm
   b. 20 μm
   c. 30 μm
   d. 40 μm
   e. None of the above

Answer: 30 μm

14. A single 0.600 μm slit has a first minimum at 60°. The wavelength of the light is:

   a. 488 nm
   b. 520 nm
   c. 580 nm
   d. 633 nm
   e. None of the above

Answer: 520 nm

15. What is the second order diffraction angle for 400nm light scattered of a diffrfaction grating having 10,000 lines/cm?

   a. 15.4^0
   b. 44.0^0
   c. 23.6^0
   d. 53.0^0
   e. None of the above

Answer: 53.0^0

16. Unpolarized light of intensity I_0 passes through two polaroids. The axis of one is vertical and the other is at 60^0 to the vertical. What is the orientation and the intensity of the transmitted light?

   a. $I_0/8$; 60^0 relative to the vertical
   b. $I_0/16$; 90^0 relative to the vertical
   c. $I_0/2$; 45^0 relative to the vertical
   d. $I_0/4$; 30^0 relative to the vertical
   e. None of the above

Answer: $I_0/8$; 60^0 relative to the vertical

17. In Young's Experiment using 632.8 nm light the slits are 0.63 mm apart. If the desired fringe spacing is 1.0 mm, the screen distance should be:

    a.   78 cm
    b.   84 cm
    c.   92 cm
    d.   100 cm
    e.   None of the above

    Answer: 100 cm

25.0 - PROBLEMS

18. Unpolarized light is incident upon three dichroic polarizers set at 0°, 30°, and 60° with respect to the vertical. (a) Calculate the percent of the incident light transmitted. (b) If the center filter is removed, calculate the percent of the incident light transmitted.

    Answer: (a) 28.1%; (b) 12.5%

19. MgF_2 ($n = 1.38$) is often used as antireflective coatings on glass lenses. If the center of the visible spectrum is 550 nm, (a) calculate the thickness of the thinnest coating for anti-reflection near normal incidence. (b) Calculate the minimum thickness of water ($n = 4/3$) for an antireflective coating on glass at near normal incidence. (c) Calculate the minimum thickness of water on glass for a reflective coating.

    Answer: (a) $0.10 \mu m$; (b) $0.10 \ \mu m$; (c) $0.21 \ \mu m$

20. Two slits, 0.16 mm apart, are illuminated with monochromatic light which causes an interference pattern on a screen 75 cm away. If the spacing between the first and eighth minima is 1.6 cm, (a) calculate the wavelength of the light. (b) Calculate the angle the eighth minimum makes with the axis of the incident light.

    Answer: (a) 488 nm; (b) 1.3°

21. A 632.8 nm laser light illuminates a narrow slit. A diffraction pattern is observed on a screen 60 cm away. If the spacing between the first and fifth minima is 32 mm, (a) calculate the distance of the first minimum from the axis of the incident light. (b) Calculate the distance of the fifth minimum from the axis of the incident light. (c) Calculate the slit width.

    Answer: (a) 8 mm; (b) 40 mm; (c) 0.475 mm

22. 588 nm laser light is incident upon a 7.5 μm slit resulting in a diffraction pattern on a screen 60 cm away. (a) Calculate the distance from the light axis to the first maximum (other than the central maximum). (b) Calculate the slit width for 632.8 nm laser light to have the same minima spacing as the 588 nm light.

    Answer: (a) 7.1 cm; (b) 8.1 μm

23. In a Young's Experiment, two slits are illuminated both by 588 nm laser light and a tunable dye laser light. On a screen, the fourth minimum of the 588 nm laser coincides with the third minimum of the dye laser. (a) Calculate the wavelength of the dye laser. (b) If the distance to the fourth minimum of the 588 nm laser is 5.0 cm measured on a screen 25 cm away, calculate the slit width.

    Answer: (a) 784 nm; (b) 12 μm

24. 488 nm laser light passes through two slits 0.15 mm apart and forms an interference pattern on a screen 1.6 m away. (a) Calculate the angle and distance to the third maximum from the axis of the light. (b) Calculate the angle and distance to the fourth minimum from the axis of the light.

    Answer: (a) 0.56°, 1.56 cm; (b) 0.65°, 1.82 cm

25. Two linear polarizers are set with their axes at 90°. (a) Calculate the percent of the light tr Ansmitted. (b) If another polarizer is inserted between them with its axis at 45° to the others, calculate the percent of unpolarized light transmitted. (c) If two additional polarizers are inserted on either side of the

third polarizer with their axis 45° to each other and 22.5° to the third polarizer, calculate the percent of unpolarized light transmitted.

Answer: (a) 0%; (b) 12.5%; (c) 26.5%

26. A radio telescope has a 0.25 cm² effective detector area with a linear polarizer to measure the polarization of radiation from stars. 7.5 nW maximum and 5.0 nW minimum intensity is measured as the polarizer is rotated. (a) Calculate the percent polarization involved. (b) Calculate the peak electric field of the radiation received.

Answer: (a) 33%; (b) 30.7 V/cm

27. Two 1000 Hz speakers are exactly in phase

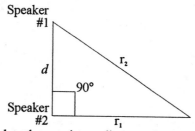

and 1.5 m apart, as shown. (a) Calculate the maximum distance along r_1 that destructive interference can occur. (b) Calculate the minimum distance along r_1 that constructive interference can occur.

Answer: (a) 6.5 m; (b) 3.1 m

28. 632.8 nm laser light is diffracted by a circular aperture 2.5 μm in diameter. The maximum, called the Airy disk, is surrounded by a dark ring observed on a screen 20 cm away. (a) Calculate the diameter of the dark ring. (b) Calculate the distance between the first minima on either side of the central maximum for diffraction from a single slit 2.5 μm wide substituted for the circular aperture.

Answer: (a) 13 cm; (b) 10 cm

29. The Rayleigh criterion is an approximation for the resolvability of two objects close together by diffraction limited optics of a given aperture, D. The criterion is that the minimum resolvable angle is to the centers of two Airy disks that just touch (i.e., $\theta_{min} = 1.22\lambda/D$). (a) Using the Rayleigh criterion, calculate the angular resolution, in seconds of arc, for sunlight (550 nm) from two objects 10 miles away as viewed through 5.0 cm aperture telescope. (b) Calculate the distance between the objects.

Answer: (a) 2.8 s of arc; (b) 22 cm

30. Using the Rayleigh criterion once again and assuming the human eye has a 3.0 mm diameter pupils, (a) calculate the distance at which two approaching yellow (575 nm) halogen headlights 1.2 m apart can be resolved. (b) Calculate the time until the oncoming car passes if you both are traveling at 60 mi/h toward one another.

Answer: (a) 5.1 km; (b) 1.6 min.

31. Two coherent 750 MHz point radio sources 80 cm apart radiate in phase. A receiver moves in a circular path of 4.0 m radius (using their midpoint as a center) completely around the sources. (a) Calculate the number of maxima in 360°. (b) If the separation is increased to 2.0 m, calculate the number of minima in 360°.

Answer: (a) 8; (b) 20

32. A soap bubble appears green ($\lambda = 540$nm) at the point on its surface nearest to the viewer. What is its minimum thickness?

Answer: 100nm

33. Light of wavelength 750nm passes through a slit 1.0μm wide. How wide is the central maximum (in centimeters) on the screen 20cm away?

34. A thin wire in front of a HeNe laser (632.8 nm) produces a diffraction pattern on a screen 125 cm away like that of a narrow slit the same width as the diameter of the wire. (a) Calculate the shift in the eighth minima when the wire, 1.5 mm in diameter, changes size by 10%. (b) Calculate the distance between the third maxima on either size of the central maximum.

Answer: (a) 0.31 mm; (b) 3.7 mm

CHAPTER 26

26.0 - MULTIPLE CHOICE QUESTIONS

1. A nuclear particle has a lifetime of 1.6 μs in the laboratory. In a high energy accelerator its lifetime is 8.0 μs. Its speed in the accelerator is:

    a.   0.96 c
    b.   0.97 c
    c.   0.98 c
    d.   0.99 c
    e.   None of the above

                                                                Answer: 0.98 c

2. A 180 m long spaceship passes a space station at a relative speed of 0.800 c. Its length according to measurements by the space station is:

    a.   88.0 m
    b.   108 m
    c.   180 m
    d.   300 m
    e.   None of the above

                                                                Answer: 108 m

3. A 180 m long spaceship passes a space station at a relative speed of 0.800 c. The time for the spaceship to pass the station is:

    a.   450 ns
    b.   500 ns
    c.   750 ns
    d.   1.25 μs
    e.   None of the above

                                                                Answer: 450 ns

4. By what percent (to two sig. figs.) would the clocks on a 1000 mi/h SST run slow?

    a. $1.6 \times 10^{-7}\%$
    b. $2.5 \times 10^{-8}\%$
    c. $3.0 \times 10^{-9}\%$
    d. $4.5 \times 10^{-10}\%$
    e.   None of the above

                                                                Answer: $4.5 \times 10^{-10}\%$

5. How much time would the watch of the pilot of a 1000 mi/h SST lose in one year (3.16×10^7 s)?

    a.   0.082 ms
    b.   0.14 ms
    c.   0.64 ms
    d.   1.2 ms
    e.   None of the above

Answer: 0.14 ms

6. A space probe leaves Earth at a speed of 0.98 c and returns ten years later. On board the probe is a culture of bacteria which doubles in population every four months. By what factor has the population increased?

    a. 24
    b. 48
    c. 64
    d. 256
    e. None of the above

Answer: 64

7. A proton ($m = 1.67 \times 10^{-27}$ kg) has a speed of 0.95 c in the laboratory. Its total energy is:

    a. 24 MeV
    b. 360 MeV
    c. 2×10^3 MeV
    d. 3×10^3 MeV
    e. None of the above

Answer: 3×10^3 MeV

8. A proton ($m = 1.67 \times 10^{-27}$ kg) has a speed of 0.95 c in the laboratory. Its kinetic energy is:

    a. 24 MeV
    b. 360 MeV
    c. 2×10^3 MeV
    d. 3×10^3 MeV
    e. None of the above

Answer: 2×10^3 MeV

9. A 3.75 eV photon has a momentum (kg · m/s) of:

    a. 2×10^{-27}
    b. 8×10^{-26}
    c. 4×10^{-24}
    d. 0
    e. None of the above

Answer: 2×10^{-27}

10. A spaceship traveling at 0.60 c fires a projectile straight ahead at 0.80 c. The speed of the projectile, as observed by a stationary space station, is:

    a. 0.88 c
    b. 0.95 c
    c. 0.98 c
    d. 1.4 c
    e. None of the above

Answer: 0.95 c

11. A spaceport observes two spaceships approaching each other head on. Both ships are traveling at 0.80 c. At what speed are they approaching each other as observed on one of the ships?

   a.   0.80 c
   b.   0.92 c
   c.   0.98 c
   d.   1.6 c
   e.   None of the above

Answer: 0.98 c

12. A spaceport observes two spaceships approaching each other head on. Both ships are traveling at 0.80 c. How fast are they approaching each other as observed by the spaceport?

   a.   0.80 c
   b.   0.92 c
   c.   0.98 c
   d.   1.6 c
   e.   None of the above

Answer: 1.6 c

13. A spaceport observes two 150 m long spaceships approaching each other head on. Both ships are traveling at 0.80 c. How long are they as determined by the spaceport?

   a.   90 m
   b.   100 m
   c.   120 m
   d.   150 m
   e.   None of the above

Answer: 90 m

14. A car traveling 100km/h covers certain distance in 10.00s according to the drivers watch. How much longer does this interval appear to the statonary observer on the side of the road?

   a. 4×10^{-14}s
   b.   1s
   c. 3×10^{-12}s
   d. 5×10^{-14}s
   e.   None of the above

Answer: 4×10^{-14}s

15. A particle called pion has mass of 2.4×10^{-28}kg and travels at speed of 2.4×10^8m/s. What is its kinetic energy?

   a. 6.9×10^{-11}J
   b. 6.9×10^{-12}J
   c. 1.4×10^{-11}J
   d. 1.4×10^{-12}J
   e.   None of the above

Answer: 1.4×10^{-11}J

16. A spaceport observes two 150 m long spaceships approaching each other head on. Both ships are traveling at 0.80 c. How long is one spaceship as determined by the other?

    a.   25 m
    b.   33 m
    c.   80 m
    d.   180 m
    e.   None of the above

Answer: 33 m

17. A spaceport observes two 150 m long spaceships approaching each other head on. Both ships are traveling at 0.80 c. How long does it take the spaceships to pass one another according to the spaceport?

    a.   94 ns
    b.   112 ns
    c.   188 ns
    d.   375 ns
    e.   None of the above

Answer: 375 ns

26.0 - PROBLEMS

18. You are traveling at 0.60 c relative to Earth. (a) Calculate the length of a meter stick that is traveling toward you at 0.80 c relative to Earth. (b) Calculate the length of the meter stick as observed from Earth.
Answer: (a) 32 cm; (b) 60 cm

19. You are traveling at 0.60 c relative to Earth and a meter stick is traveling toward you at 0.80 c relative to Earth. (a) Calculate the time for the meter stick to pass you. (b) Calculate the time for the meter stick to pass you as observed from Earth.
Answer: (a) 1.1 ns; (b) 2.5 ns

20. A spaceship departs Earth at 0.950 c for the star Alpha Centauri 4.00 light years away from Earth. (a) Calculate the time for the spaceship to reach the star as computed on Earth. (b) Calculate the distance to the star and the time to reach it as determined by the spaceship. (c) Calculate the time lapse on Earth after 1.00 y elapses on the spaceship's clocks as determined on the spaceship.
Answer: (a) 4.21 yr; (b) 1.25 c-yr, 1.32 y; (c) 0.312 y

21. If it requires 4.2 eV to break the NaCl molecule into its atomic parts of Na (23 g/mol) and Cl (35.5 g/mol), (a) calculate the mass lost by the atoms when forming the molecule. (b) Calculate the percent of the mass of the atoms that goes into the bonding of the molecule.
Answer: (a) 7.5×10^{-36} kg; (b) $7.7 \times 10^{-9}\%$

22. (a) Calculate the work that must be done (classically) to accelerate an electron ($m = 9.1 \times 10^{-31}$ kg) from rest to the speed of light. (b) Calculate (relativistically) the actual speed the electron would attain for this amount of work.
Answer: (a) 4.1×10^{-14} J; (b) 0.745 c

23. An electron has a total energy of 2.75 MeV. (a) Calculate its momentum. (b) Calculate its speed.
Answer: (a) 1.44×10^{-21} kg · m/s; (b) 2.95×10^8 m/s

24. A 1.75 MeV electron moves on a semicircle of 5.00 cm radius in a uniform magnetic flux. (a) Calculate the speed of the electron. (b) Calculate the magnitude of the magnetic flux.

180

25. A space patrol starship traveling at 0.500 c is chasing a renegade spaceship traveling at 0.750 c. The starship fires a projectile with a muzzle speed of 0.400 c at the renegade 45.0 c-sec ahead. (a) Calculate, classically, the time for the projectile to impact the renegade. (b) Calculate the actual time for the projectile to impact.

    Answer: (a) 300 s; (b) ∞

26. (a) From the definition of relativistic energy, derive the expression for the relativity factor, γ, as $\gamma = 1 + KE/mc^2$. (b) Calculate γ for an electron ($m = 9.10 \times 10^{-27}$ kg) accelerated through a potential of 1.00×10^7 V. (c) Calculate γ for a proton accelerated through the same potential.

    Answer: (b) 20.5; (c) 1.01

27. (a) From the definition of relativistic momentum, derive the relationship $vE = pc^2$, where E is the total energy. (b) Use this expression to find the ratio of the classical momentum to the relativistic momentum for the 10.0 MeV electron.

    Answer: (b) 5.12×10^{-2}

28. (a) From the definition of relativistic energy and momentum, and using the relativistic energy triangle (solving for pc) for the case where $\gamma \gg 1$, derive the approximation $v = c(1 - 1/2\gamma^2)$. (b) Using this approximation, calculate the speed of the 10.0 MeV electron.

    Answer: (b) 0.999 c

29. The relativistic Doppler Effect is given as $f = f_0[(1 - \beta)/(1 + \beta)]^{1/2}$, where $\beta = v/c$ for a source of rest frequency f_0 and receding from the observer at a speed v. The signs are reversed in the numerator and denominator for an approaching source. (a) Calculate the frequency at which a 360 MHz radio signal from a spaceship traveling at 0.800 c away from Earth will be received. (b) Calculate the frequency that Earth should us to answer the signal if the spaceship is tuned to 360 MHz.

    Answer: (a) 120 MHz ; (b) 1080 MHz

30. A distant galaxy is moving away from Earth at 0.25 c. Calculate the fractional red shift, $(\lambda - \lambda_0)/\lambda_0$, for all frequencies of rest wavelength, λ_0.

    Answer: 0.29

31. A spaceship returning to Earth at 0.200 c uses a red He-Ne laser (632.8 nm) to send a signal to Earth. (a) Calculate the wavelength and color of the received signal. (b) If the spaceship is 2.40 c-days from Earth when it sends the signal, calculate the time it takes the signal to arrive.

    Answer: (a) 517 nm, green; (b) 57.6 h

32. A person in a rocket traveling at 0.5c (with respect to the earth) observes a meteor come from behind and pass her at a speed she measures as 0.50c. How fast is the meteor moving relative to the earth?

    Answer: 0.80c

33. The period of a pendulum fixed on earth is 2.00s. What would be the pendulum's period when traveling on a spaceship at $v = 2.00 \times 10^8$ m/s as measured (a) on earth, and (b) on the spaceship?

    Answer: (a) 2.68s; (b) 2.00s

34. Pions (rest energy 139.6 MeV) are created by cosmic rays 110 km above the Earth with a total energy of 140 GeV and an at rest decay time of 35 ns. (a) Calculate the time for the pion to decay. (b) If the pion travels directly toward Earth, calculate the altitude for the decay.

    Answer: (a) 35 μs; (b) 99.5 km

CHAPTER 27

27.0 - MULTIPLE CHOICE QUESTIONS

1. The number of faradays, F, of charge required to deposit 0.25 g of copper (63.5 g/mole) from a solution of $CuSO_4$ is:

    a. $4.0 \times 10^{-3}F$
    b. $8.0 \times 10^{-3}F$
    c. $16 \times 10^{-3}F$
    d. $25 \times 10^{-3}F$
    e. None of the above

    Answer: $8.0 \times 10^{-3}F$

2. The current required to deposit 0.25 g of copper above in 5 min is:

    a. 1.0 A
    b. 1.25 A
    c. 2.5 A
    d. 5.0 A
    e. None of the above

    Answer: 2.5 A

3. The charge to mass ratio for an alpha particle is:

    a. 8.0×10^{-18} C/kg
    b. 3.5×10^4 C/kg
    c. 1.2×10^7 C/kg
    d. 4.8×10^7 C/kg
    e. None of the above

    Answer: 4.8×10^7 C/kg

4. The wavelength of the most energetic photon to ionize atomic hydrogen in the Balmer series is:

    a. 365 nm
    b. 434 nm
    c. 486 nm
    d. 656 nm
    e. None of the above

    Answer: 365 nm

5. The wavelength of the least energetic photon absorbed in the Lyman series of atomic hydrogen is:

    a. 91 nm
    b. 97 nm
    c. 104 nm
    d. 122 nm
    e. None of the above

6.   The wavelength of the least energetic photon absorbed in the Paschen series of atomic hydrogen is:

   a.   762 nm
   b.   820 nm
   c.   1240 nm
   d.   1875 nm
   e.   None of the above

Answer: 1875 nm

7.   Monochromatic X-rays experience first order Bragg reflection in a crystal at an angle of 1.6°. The second order reflection would occur at:

   a.   1.8°
   b.   2.4°
   c.   3.2°
   d.   4.8°
   e.   None of the above

Answer: 3.2°

8.   A crystal is oriented so that there is 0.17 nm between Bragg planes. The third order reflection of 0.08 nm X-rays occurs at an angle of:

   a.   16°
   b.   24°
   c.   32°
   d.   45°
   e.   None of the above

Answer: 45°

9.   CsCl has eight atoms at the corners of a cube with 0.411 nm sides and an atom at the center of the cube. The largest angle at which first order Bragg reflection occurs for 0.10 nm X-rays is:

   a.   14°
   b.   16°
   c.   18°
   d.   24°
   e.   None of the above

Answer: 14°

10.   The normal to a CsCl crystal is parallel to the body diagonal of the cube. Using the data of the previous question, the angle from this normal at which first order Bragg reflection occurs is:

   a.   8.1°
   b.   16.7°
   c.   41°
   d.   82°
   e.   None of the above

11. An early Bragg experiment was conducted with rock salt (NaCl) which has a cube structure with atoms at the corners and on the center of the faces and edges with a cube edge of 0.563 nm. The largest first order Bragg reflection occurred at 5°. The wavelength of the X-ray was:

   a.   0.05 nm
   b.   0.08 nm
   c.   0.12 nm
   d.   0.18 nm
   e.   None of the above

Answer: 0.05 nm

12. A beam of alpha particles of cross-sectional area 0.17 cm^2 strikes a 2.0 μm thick gold foil (197 g/mole and density 19.3 g/cm^3). The number of atoms of gold in the path of the beam is:

   a. 4.2×10^{16}
   b. 8.2×10^{16}
   c. 2.0×10^{18}
   d. 5.9×10^{22}
   e.   None of the above

Answer: 2.0×10^{18}

13. An AgCN solution is used to electroplate silver. How much charge is required to plate out 0.360 g of silver (109 g/mole)?

   a.   180 C
   b.   245 C
   c.   320 C
   d.   480 C
   e.   None of the above

Answer: 320 C

14. An AgCN solution is used to electroplate silver. If 0.36 g of silver (109 g/mole) is plated out, the number of Ag atoms transferred is:

   a. 8×10^{20}
   b. 2×10^{21}
   c. 8×10^{21}
   d. 2×10^{22}
   e.   None of the above

Answer: 2×10^{21}

15. Approximately, how many protons would you get if you bought 1g of them?

   a. 6×10^{24}
   b. 1×10^{21}
   c. 5×10^{59}
   d. 2×10^{27}
   e.   None of the above

16. What is the longest wavelength in Balmer series?

    a.   656.3nm
    b.   365.0nm
    c.   895.4nm
    d.   208.5nm
    e.   None of the above

    Answer: 656.3nm

17. An AgCN solution is used to electroplate silver. If 0.36 g of silver (109 g/mole) is plated out, the mass of the Ag atom is:

    a. 1.8×10^{-22}
    b. 2.4×10^{-22}
    c. 8.8×10^{-22}
    d. 2.0×10^{-21}
    e.   None of the above

    Answer: 1.8×10^{-22}

27.0 - PROBLEMS

18. A crystal of lead sulfide (PbS) has a set of Bragg planes 0.296 nm apart. If 0.0850 nm X-rays are used, (a) calculate the angle between the incident and first order reflected beam. (b) Calculate the order of the Bragg reflection for a reflected beam making an angle of 92° with the incident beam.
    Answer: (a) 16.5°; (b) 5

19. Cesium chloride (CsCl) has a cube shaped crystal structure with 4.11 Å sides. Atoms are located at the corners of the cube and in the center of the cube. As the cube is rotated about an axis normal to one face of the cube, two reflection minima between an incident 90° beam and a reflected beams is noted at 15.82° and 22.45°. (a) Calculate the wavelength of the X-rays. (b) Calculate the corresponding angles between incident and reflected beams for third order Bragg reflection.
    Answer: (a) 0.080 nm; (b) 48.8°, 71.5°

20. In the Debye-Scherrer method, the Bragg reflection occurs for a powered collection of

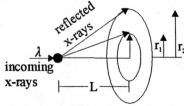

    single crystals resulting in rings as the solutions to Bragg's equation for all possible orientations. (a) Derive an equation for the radius of the rings, r, in terms of the order of reflection, and reflecting plane spacing, d, and λ and L, as shown. (b) For 0.060 nm X-rays and CsCl, calculate the first order Bragg reflection rings radii for the three smallest diameter rings for $L = 20$ cm.
    Answer: (a) $r = m\lambda L/2d$; (b) 1.69 cm, 2.06 cm, 2.92 cm

21. From Rutherford scattering, the distance to the closest point of approach of alpha particles is $R = 2kZe^2/(KE)$, where k is the Coulomb constant and Z is the number of nuclear charges of the

scatterer. (a) Calculate the closest point of approach of a 10.0 MeV alpha particle scattering by a Au nucleus ($Z = 79$). (b) Calculate the ratio of the speed of the alpha particle to the velocity of light.

Answer: (a) 22.8 fm; (b) 7.3×10^{-2}

22. Using Rutherford scattering, (a) calculate the closest point of approach of a 5.00 MeV alpha particle to an Al nucleus ($Z = 13$). (b) If Al has a nuclear radius of 4.00 fm, calculate the energy the alpha particle needs to just reach the surface of the nucleus for a head-on collision.

Answer: (a) 74.9 fm; (b) 9.36 MeV

23. If a hydrogen atom is in its ground state (lowest electron energy), (a) calculate the wavelength of the photon absorbed to put the electron in the second energy level above the ground state. (b) Calculate the photon emitted as the electron drops down to the next lower energy level.

Answer: (a) 103 nm; (b) 656 nm

24. A solution of copper sulfate ($CuSO_4$) is used for plating out copper (9.00 g/cm^3 and 63.5 g/mol). (a) Calculate the number of moles of copper needed to plate a 2.50 cm^2 area to a thickness of 5.00 μm. (b) Calculate the amp-sec required.

Answer: (a) 1.77×10^{-4} mol; (b) 34.2 A $\cdot$ s

25. A muon can be considered a heavy electron having a rest mass of 105.7 MeV. (a) Calculate the muon's charge to mass ratio. (b) If the muon, at rest, decays into a 52.3 MeV electron (and neutrinos), calculate the energy left over.

Answer: (a) 8.52×10^8 C/kg; (b) 53.4 MeV

26. Polychromatic X-rays with wavelengths from 0.025 nm to 0.100 nm are Bragg reflected from a crystal with planes 0.164 nm apart at a fixed angle of 36° relative to the incident beam. (a) Calculate the shortest usable wavelength and the order of the reflection. (b) If another set of planes 0.284 nm apart are examined, calculate the shortest usable wavelength and the order of the reflection.

Answer: (a) 0.025 nm, 4; (b) 0.025 nm, 7

27. Using Lyman's formula for the spectrum of H-atom determine the wavelength of the light emitted by the transition from n = 2 to n = 1.

Answer: 122nm

28. Monochromatic 0.0800 nm X-rays are used to examine a crystal with Bragg planes 0.135 nm apart. (a) Calculate the usable angles of Bragg reflection relative to the incident radiation. (b) Another set of planes 0.234 nm apart are to be examined, calculate the usable angles of the Bragg reflection relative to the incident radiation.

Answer: (a) 34.5°, 72.7°, 125.5°; (b) 19.7°, 40°, 61.7°, 86.3°, 117.5°

29. In the Thompson experiment, the speed, v_x,

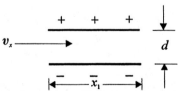

of the electron is measured by adjusting the voltage, V, between two plates, d, apart to counteract the deflection of a magnetic flux (into page) so that the electron passes through a distance, x, undeflected. (a) Derive the equation for v_x and the time of transit, t, in terms of these parameters. (b) Calculate v_x and t, for $V = 45$ V, $d = 1.2$ cm, $x_1 = 5.0$ cm, and $B = 1.5$ gauss.

Answer: (a) $v_x = V/dB$, $t_1 = x_1 dB/V$; (b) 2.5×10^7 m/s, 2.0 ns

30. Continuing the Thompson experiment, when the

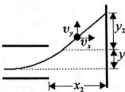

magnetic flux is turned off, the electric field deflects the electron a distance, y_1, while it is between the field plates. (a) Derive an equation for y_1 in terms of x_1, v_x, (e/m) and parameters of the problem. (b) Derive an equation for y_2 in terms of x_1, x_2, v_x, (e/m) and parameters of the problem. (c) Solve for (e/m) for the parameters of the previous problem and $x_2 = 30$ cm and $y_2 = 1.53$ cm.

Answer: (a) $y_1 = \frac{1}{2}(e/m)(V/d)(x_1/v_x)^2$; (b) $y_2 = (e/m)(V/d)(x_1 x_2/v_x^2)$; (c) 1.7×10^{11} C/kg

31. In the Millikan oil-drop experiment, a charged oil droplet is raised against gravity by an electric field. (a) Derive a formula for the magnitude of electric field, E, that will cause the rise time to equal the field-free fall time in the field of view (neglect drag and buoyancy). (b) Evaluate your result for a spherical oil droplet of density 0.943 g/cm^3, radius 2.75 μm, and $q = 5e$.

Answer: (a) $E = 2\ mg/q$; (b) 2.0×10^6 V/m

32. In the Millikan oil-drop experiment, the drag force given by Stokes' law as $F = 6\pi\eta rv$ must be included where η is the viscosity of air, r is the radius of the droplet, and v its speed. (a) Write an equation for the speed, v_1, that a droplet falls in the absence of an electric field. (b) Write an equation for the speed, v_2, that a droplet rises with the electric field present. (c) Using these two speeds, write an equation for the charge on the droplet.

Answer: (a) $v_1 = mg/6\pi\eta$; (b) $v_2 = (qE - mg)6\pi a$; (c) $q = (mg/E)\left(\frac{v_1 + v_2}{v_1}\right)$

33. Crystalography is performed using x-rays. Assume that instead we try to use ultraviolet light. Consider a crystal with spacing between atomic planes equal to 0.27nm. If a beam of almost monochrmomatic UV light of wavelength of 150nm is incident on the crystal at what angle we will see the first order diffraction maximum?

Answer: We will not see any diffraction scattering!

34. In the Millikan oil-drop experiment, the drag force given by Stokes' law as $F = 6\pi\eta rv$ must be included where η is the viscosity of air, r is the radius of the droplet, and v its speed. Using the provided information and the measured values $v_1 = 8.68 \times 10^{-4}$ m/s, $v_2 = 2.04 \times 10^{-5}$ m/s when $E = 6.45 \times 10^5$ V/m with $\eta = 1.825 \times 10^{-5}$ N $\cdot$ s/m^2, and the data of the previous problems, calculate the charge on the droplet.

Answer: 1.28×10^{-18} C

CHAPTER 28

28.0 - MULTIPLE CHOICE QUESTIONS

1. The temperature of a blackbody radiator with a wavelength maximum of 9.9 μm is:

    a.   20° C
    b.   25° C
    c.   273 K
    d.   300 K
    e.   None of the above

    Answer: 20° C

2. If the temperature of a blackbody radiator is doubled, the power is increased by a factor of:

    a.   8
    b.   16
    c.   32
    d.   64
    e.   None of the above

    Answer: 16

3. The total power emitted by a 1000° C blackbody radiator of 1.35 cm^2 area is:

    a.   12.0 μW
    b.   16.1 MW
    c.   0.727 W
    d.   20.1 W
    e.   None of the above

    Answer: 20.1 W

4. The heat energy radiated per hour by a 1.63 m^2 area steam radiator at 100° C into a room at 20° C, if the emissivity is 0.75, is:

    a.   833 J
    b.   480 kJ
    c.   3.0 MJ
    d.   4.5 MJ
    e.   None of the above

    Answer: 3.0 MJ

5. A 40 kV X-ray tube has a minimum wavelength of radiation of:

    a.   0.012 nm
    b.   0.023 nm
    c.   0.031 nm
    d.   0.048 nm
    e.   None of the above

    Answer: 0.031 nm

6.   What voltage is required to produce 0.083 nm or longer wavelength photons in an X-ray tube?

   a.   12 kV
   b.   15 kV
   c.   18 kV
   d.   20 kV
   e.   None of the above

                                                Answer: 15 kV

7.   In the photoelectric experiment, the maximum kinetic energy of electrons when the anode current stops when -1.2 volts is applied relative to the cathode is:

   a. -1.2 eV
   b.   1.2 eV
   c.   4.8 J
   d.   Can not be determined
   e.   None of the above

                                                Answer: 1.2 eV

8.   In the photoelectric experiment, the current ceases as the wavelength of the monochromatic light is increased to 445 nm. The work function of the cathode is:

   a.   1.63 eV
   b.   2.46 eV
   c.   2.79 eV
   d.   4.22 eV
   e.   None of the above

                                                Answer: 2.79 eV

9.   The change in wavelength of photons Compton scattered at 60° is:

   a.   1.2 pm
   b.   8.2 pm
   c.   15 pm
   d.   24 pm
   e.   None of the above

                                                Answer: 1.2 pm

10.   When 500 nm light falls on a potassium cathode (work function 2.2 eV) the maximum kinetic energy of the emitted electrons is:

   a.   0.28 eV
   b.   0.56 eV
   c.   1.2 eV
   d.   2.4 eV
   e.   None of the above

                                                Answer: 0.28 eV

11.   The number of photons per second emitted by a 75 kW transmitter tuned to 1260 kHz is:

a. 4×10^{24}
b. 7×10^{29}
c. 4×10^{30}
d. 9×10^{31}
e. None of the above

Answer: 9×10^{31}

12. Zinc has a work function of 4.25 eV. The threshold frequency for photoemission is:

a. 2.4×10^{14} Hz
b. 8.2×10^{14} Hz
c. 1.0×10^{15} Hz
d. 4.2×10^{15} Hz
e. None of the above

Answer: 1.0×10^{15} Hz

13. The Compton wavelength of the scattering of electrons from protons ($m = 1.67 \times 10^{-27}$ kg) would be:

a. 2.4 pm
b. 4.8×10^{-1} pm
c. 9.6×10^{-2} pm
d. 1.3×10^{-3} pm
e. None of the above

Answer: 1.3×10^{-3} pm

14. The maximum Compton shift of wavelength of photons scattered by electrons is:

a. 2.4 pm
b. 4.8 pm
c. 7.2 pm
d. 9.6 pm
e. None of the above

Answer: 4.8 pm

15. What is the wavelength of an electron that has been accelerated through a potential difference of 100V?

a. 1.6×10^{-10}m
b. 0.4×10^{-11}m
c. 1.8×10^{-15}m
d. 1.2×10^{-10}m
e. None of the above

Answer: 1.2×10^{-10}m

16. What is the minimum energy of a photon that can produce an electron-positron pair?

a. 2.04 MeV
b. 1.02 MeV
c. 7.32 keV
d. 0.511 keV

e.   None of the above

Answer: 1.02 MeV

17.   If photons strike a potassium cathode (work function 2.2 eV) and cause a photo-current which can be cut-off with -4.0 V applied to the anode with respect to the cathode, the wavelength of the incident photons is:

a.   165 nm
b.   180 nm
c.   200 nm
d.   225 nm
e.   None of the above

Answer: 200 nm

28.0 - PROBLEMS

18.   A thermonuclear explosion has a fireball 10 km in diameter at a temperature of 1.0×10^7 K. (a) Considering this a black body radiator, calculate the wavelength of maximum spectral radiance. (b) Calculate the power radiated.

Answer: (a) 0.29 mn; (b) 1.8×10^{29} W

19.   If the work function of a metal is 1.82 eV, (a) calculate the stopping potential in the photoelectric effect for 325 nm photons. (b) Calculate the maximum speed of the emitted photoelectrons.

Answer: (a) 2.0 V; (b) 8.4×10^5 m/s

20.   The stopping potential of photoelectrons is 0.45 V at 548 nm. The wavelength is changed and a new stopping potential of 2.36 V is found. (a) Calculate the work function of the cathode surface. (b) Calculate the second wavelength.

Answer: (a) 1.8 eV; (b) 297 nm

21.   For a metal cathode, one obtains experimentally stopping potentials of 0.55 V at 450 nm and 1.75 V at 315 nm for photoelectrons. (a) Calculate Planck's constant from this data. (b) Calculate the work function of the cathode surface.

Answer: (a) 6.72×10^{-34} Js; (b) 2.2 eV

22.   0.511 MeV gamma ray photons are Compton scattered at an angle of 45°. (a) Calculate the wavelength of the scattered photons. (b) Calculate the kinetic energy of the recoiling electron.

Answer: (a) 2.36 pm; (b) 15.4 keV

23.   62 keV X-rays are Compton scattered and experience a frequency shift of $1.21 \times 10^{-3}\%$. (a) Calculate the scattering angle of the photons. (b) Calculate the kinetic energy of the recoiling electron.

Answer: (a) 90°; (b) 0.75 eV

24.   250 keV X-rays are Compton scattered and lose 12.5 % of their energy to the scattering electron. (a) Calculate the scattering angle of the X-rays. (b) Calculate the momentum of the scattered X-ray.

Answer: (a) 45°; (b) 219 keV/c

25.   The gas from a jet engine exits at about 2000° C and cools to 10% of this temperature behind the jet. (a) If SAM missiles are designed to target these trailing gases, calculate the wavelength of greatest sensitivity of the detector. (b) Calculate the energy of these exhaust photons to which the detector is most sensitive.

Answer: (a) 6.13 μm; (b) 0.20 eV

26. The work function for a silver surface is $W_0 = 4.73 \text{eV}$. What is the minimum frequency that the light must have to eject electrons from this surface?

Answer: $1.14 \times 10^{15} Hz$.

27. In the Bohr model of the hydrogen atom, the electron circles the proton in an orbit of radius, r. (a) Write an equation for the kinetic energy of the electron in terms of r. (b) Write an equation for the potential energy between the electron and proton in terms of r. (c) Write the total energy of the electron in terms of r. (d) Calculate the total energy of the electron in orbit for $r = 0.0529$ nm.

Answer: (a) $\text{KE} = ke^2/2r$; (b) $\text{PE} = -ke^2/r$; (c) $\text{U} = -ke^2/2r$; (d) -13.6 eV

28. Bohr found that quantum angular moment is given as $L = nh/2\pi$ where $n = 1, 2, 3, ...$ integer. (a) Derive an equation for the angular momentum of the electron in orbit of radius, r, classically in terms of known parameters. (Hint: use the results of kinetic energy.) (b) Using Bohr's quantum momentum as equal to the classical momentum, derive an equation for r in terms of n and known parameters. (c) Solve for r when $n = 1$.

Answer: (a) $L = [ke^2mr]^{1/2}$; (b) $r = n^2[\epsilon_0 h^2/\pi m e^2]$; (c) 0.053 nm

29. A 435.1 nm wavelength photon is emitted from an excited hydrogen gas. (a) Find the transitions involved using the Bohr model. (b) To which of the earlier radiation series of hydrogen does this transition belong?

Answer: (a) $n = 5$ to $n = 2$; (b) Balmer

30. An electron on the hydrogen atom makes a transition from $n = 3$ to $n = 1$. (a) Calculate the energy of the photon emitted. (b) Calculate the recoil speed of the atom emitting the photon.

Answer: (a) 12.1 eV; (b) 3.86 m/s

31. The Bohr model can be used for multi-proton nuclei with a single electron in orbit by replacing the charge of the proton, e, with Ze, the charge of Z protons in the nucleus. (a) Calculate the ground state ($n = 1$) energy of helium ($Z = 2$). (b) Calculate the first excited state energy ($n = 2$) of lithium ($Z = 3$).

Answer: (a) -54.4 eV; (b) -30.6 eV

32. What is the maximum kinetic energy and speed of an electron ejected from a sodium surface whose work function is $W_0 = 2.28 \text{eV}$ when illuminated by light of wavelength 410nm?

Answer: K.E. $= 1.2 \times 10^{-19}$J; v $= 5.1 \times 10^5$ m/s

33. Moseley showed that the frequency of X-rays produced from multi-proton nuclei for the Lyman series (K_α lines) can be represented as $f^{1/2} = A_n(Z - 1)$ where A_n is a constant depending on the quantum number, n, and $(Z - 1)$ replaces Z in the Bohr model. Using the Bohr model derive an expression for A_n in terms of the quantum number, n, and known parameters.

Answer: $A_n = [(me^4/8\epsilon_0^2 h^3)(1 - 1/n^2)]^{1/2}$

34. Using the previous results, calculate the wavelength of the X-ray line from copper ($Z = 29$) for the $n = 2$ to $n = 1$ transition.

Answer: 0.155 nm

CHAPTER 29

1. The speed of the electron in orbit in the ground state of the Bohr model of hydrogen is:

    a. 7.2×10^5 m/s
    b. 9.6×10^5 m/s
    c. 2.2×10^6 m/s
    d. 6.4×10^6 m/s
    e.   None of the above

    Answer: 2.2×10^6 m/s

2. The number of electrons in the L shell is:

    a.   2
    b.   6
    c.   14
    d.   18
    e.   None of the above

    Answer: None of the above

3. How many orbital magnetic quantum states are available to $4f$ electrons?

    a.   3
    b.   5
    c.   7
    d.   9
    e.   None of the above

    Answer: 7

4. The deBroglie wavelength of a 27 g bullet traveling at 1000 ft/s is:

    a. 8×10^{-35} m
    b. 2×10^{-34} m
    c. 4×10^{-34} m
    d. 6×10^{-33} m
    e.   None of the above

    Answer: 8×10^{-35} m

5. If the hydrogen nucleus is confined to a region of two Bohr radii, its uncertainty in momentum is approximately:

    a.   8 keV/c
    b.   12 keV/c
    c.   36 keV/c
    d.   0.51 MeV/c
    e.   None of the above

    Answer: 12 keV/c

6. How many orbital and spin states are available to 1d electrons
   a. 15
   b. 3
   c. 0
   d. 6
   e. None of the above

   Answer: 0

7. The deBroglie wavelength of a 150 eV electron is:

   a. 40 pm
   b. 75 pm
   c. 100 pm
   d. 120 pm
   e. None of the above

   Answer: 100 pm

8. The deBroglie wavelength of a 3.10 eV photon is:

   a. 400 nm
   b. 480 nm
   c. 520 nm
   d. 640 nm
   e. None of the above

   Answer: 400 nm

9. The deBroglie wavelength of a 8 MeV alpha particle is:

   a. 8 fm
   b. 0.4 fm
   c. 0.08 fm
   d. 0.005 fm
   e. None of the above

   Answer: 0.005 fm

10. The deBroglie wavelength of a 25 MeV electron is:

    a. 0.05 pm
    b. 0.10 pm
    c. 0.15 pm
    d. 0.25 pm
    e. None of the above

    Answer: 0.05 pm

11. A HeNe laser (632.8 nm) has the electron in the inverted state 1×10^{-8} s before it moves to a lower state. The percent that the resulting emission line is broadened is:

    a. 5×10^{-6}
    b. 2×10^{-5}

c. 8×10^{-4}
d. 4×10^{-3}
e.   None of the above

Answer: 2×10^{-5}

12.   The ground state electronic configuration of silicon ($Z = 14$) is:

a. $3p^4$
b. $1s^2 2s^2 3s^2 3p^6 3d^2$
c. $1s^2 2s^2 2p^6 3s^2 3p^4$
d. $1s^2 2s^2 2p^6 3s^2 3p^2$
e.   None of the above

Answer: $1s^2 2s^2 2p^6 3s^2 3p^2$

13.   An electron moves in a straight line with constant speed of 1.10×10^6 m/s which has been measure with a precision of 0.1%. What is the maximum precision with which its position could be simultaneously measured?

a. 1.06×10^{-7} m
b. 1.06×10^{-5} m
c. 3.14×10^{-17} m
d. 2.54×10^{-3} m
e.   None of the above

Answer: 1.06×10^{-7} m

14.   What is the shortest-wavelength X-ray photon emitted in an X-ray tube subject to 50kV?

a.   0.025mm
b.   25nm
c.   0.314nm
d.   0.025nm
e.   None of the above

Answer: 0.025nm

15.   The number of electrons that can occupy states in the M shell is:

a.   12
b.   18
c.   24
d.   34
e.   None of the above

Answer: 18

16.   If an electron's position can be measured to an accuracy of ± 0.1 nm, its speed can be determined to an accuracy of plus or minus:

a. 6×10^5 m/s
b. 9×10^5 m/s
c. 4×10^6 m/s

d. 7×10^6 m/s

e.   None of the above

Answer: 7×10^6 m/s

17.   What is the energy of an X-ray with the same momentum as a 16 eV electron?

a.   900 eV
b.   2 keV
c.   4 keV
d.   16 keV
e.   None of the above

Answer: 4 keV

29.0 - PROBLEMS

18.   (a) Using the deBroglie relation, show that classical angular momentum is quantized in units of $\hbar(h/2\pi)$, i.e., $L = \hbar, 2\hbar \dots n\hbar$, if multiples of wavelength must just fit around an orbit of radius, r. (b) Calculate the orbital angular momentum of electrons in the third Bohr orbit.

Answer: (b) 3.16×10^{-34} kg $\cdot$ m^2/s

19.   For the one dimensional box with infinite

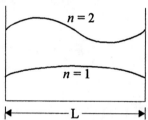

sides with resonant states $n = 1, 2, \dots$ etc, as shown. (a) Use the deBroglie relation to derive an expression for the quantized momentum of these states. (b) Derive an expression for the quantized energy of these states.

Answer: (a) $p = nh/2L$; (b) E $= n^2h^2/8mL^2$

20.   Consider a one dimensional box with infinite sides with $m = 10$ pg, $v = 0.25$ m/s, and $L = 2.65$ nm. (a) Calculate the quantum number of the ground state. (b) Calculate the energy of the ground state.

Answer: (a) 2×10^{10}; (b) 1.95 keV

21.   Consider a one dimensional box with infinite sides with $m = 10.0$ pg, $v = 0.250$ m/s, and $L = 2.65$ nm and $\Delta x/L = 0.10\%$, $\Delta p/p = 0.25\%$. (a) Calculate $\Delta x \Delta p$ for the infinite box in the ground state. (b) Calculate $\Delta x \Delta p/h$.

Answer: (a) 1.66×10^{-29} Js; (b) 2.5×10^4

22.   Consider a one dimensional box with infinite sides with $m = 10$ pg, $v = 0.25$ m/s, and $L = 2.65$ nm and an electron confined in it, (a) calculate the width of the box if the $n = 2$ state has an energy 24 eV. (b) Calculate the wavelength of the photon emitted as the electron returns to the ground state.

Answer: (a) 0.25 nm; (b) 18 eV

23.   Rutherford used 7.7 MeV alpha particles ($m = 6.68 \times 10^{-27}$ kg) to bombard the gold foil. (a) Calculate the wavelength of the alpha particles. An atomic nucleus has a radius $R = r_0 A^{1/3}$ where $r_0 = 1.2$ fm and A is the sum of neutrons and protons ($A = 197$ for Au). (b) Calculate the diameter of the Au atom.

Answer: (a) 5.2 fm; (b) 14 fm

197

24. (a) Calculate the speed of an electron which has a wavelength equal to a Compton wavelength. (b) Calculate the accelerating potential required.

Answer: (a) $c/\sqrt{2}$; (b) 210 kV

25. In the Davisson-Germer Experiment, the diffraction

of electrons at an angle $\phi = 2\alpha = 50°$ was measured for nickel atoms $D = 0.215$ nm apart, as shown. (a) Calculate the Bragg angle and the wavelength of the first order Bragg reflection of X-ray from this orientation. (b) Starting with the Bragg equation derive the Davisson-Germer diffraction equation for the reflection of electrons. Calculate the wavelength of the first order diffracted electrons.

Answer: (a) 65°, 0.165 nm; (b) $\lambda = D \sin\phi$, 0.165 nm

26. In another Davisson-Germer Experiment the diffraction of 50 eV electrons from MgO had a maximum at 55.6°. (a) Calculate the diffraction spacing. (b) Calculate the diffraction angle, ϕ, for 120 eV electrons from MgO.

Answer: (a) 0.11 nm; (b) 32.2°

27. In another Davisson-Germer Experiment the diffraction of 50.0 eV electrons from MgO had a maximum at 55.6°. (a) Calculate the angle of second order diffraction maximum for 250 eV electrons in MgO. (b) Calculate the accelerating potential required to observe third order diffraction maximum at 80.0°.

Answer: (a) 47.6°; (b) 316 V

28. An electron and photon have the same wavelength of 125 pm. (a) Calculate the momenta of each. (b) Calculate the energy of the electron and photon.

Answer: (a) 10 keV/c for both; (b) 96 eV, 10 keV

29. Singly charged phosphorus atoms (31.0 g/mol) are accelerated from rest through a 480 V potential. (a) Calculate the momentum acquired by the ions. (b) Calculate the deBroglie wavelength of the ions.

Answer: (a) 5.27 MeV/c; (b) 236 fm

30. The ionization (binding) energy of the outermost electron in boron is 8.26eV. Determine the "effective" charge seen by the electron. (Use Bohr's model!) What is the average orbital radius?

Answer: 1.56e; 0.136nm

31. An X-ray tube operates at 100kV with a current of 20mA and nearly all electron energy goes into heat. If the specific heat capacity of the 78g plate is 0.11kcal/kg · ^{0}C, what will be the temperature rise per minute if no cooling water is used?

Answer: 3,300^{0}C/min

32. Suppose ^{57}Fe emits a 1.00 MeV gamma ray and recoils in the process reducing the energy of the emitted gamma ray due to this recoil. (a) Calculate the recoil momentum. (b) Calculate the recoil energy of the iron atom.

Answer: (a) 5.33×10^{-22} kg · m/s; (b) 9.4 eV

CHAPTER 30

1. The mass of tritium is 3.016 atomic units. Its mass in MeV/c^2 is:

    a. 5.00×10^{-27}
    b.   0.0313
    c.   482
    d.   2809
    e.   None of the above

    Answer: 2809

2. The diameter of a gold nucleus ($Z = 79$, $A = 197$) is computed in fm to be:

    a.   1.7
    b.   7.0
    c.   14
    d.   19
    e.   None of the above

    Answer: 14

3. The diameter of a gold nucleus is $Z = 79$, $A = 197$. Au has how many neutrons?

    a.   79
    b.   118
    c.   156
    d.   197
    e.   None of the above

    Answer: 118

4. If the radius of a nucleus is measured to be 3.024 fm, the element is:

    a. ^{3}H
    b. ^{6}Li
    c. ^{14}N
    d. ^{20}Ne
    e.   None of the above

    Answer: None of the above

5. The mass of a proton is 938.28 MeV/c^2 and a neutron 939.57 MeV/c^2. The rest mass of a tritium nucleus is 2 808.92 MeV/c^2. The binding energy per nucleon of tritium is (in MeV):

    a.   1.34
    b.   2.84
    c.   8.03
    d.   16.1
    e.   None of the above

    Answer: 2.84

6.   An electron and positron collide and annihilate one another, the energy released is:

       a.   1.0 MeV
       b.   2.5 MeV
       c.   5.0 MeV
       d.   10 MeV
       e.   None of the above

                                                      Answer: 1.0 MeV

7.   The bombardment of beryllium $\left(^{9}_{4}Be\right)$ target by alpha particles produces a neutron. The other reaction product is:

       a.   2He
       b.   B
       c.   C
       d.   O
       e.   None of the above

                                                      Answer: C

8.   The beta decay of tritium yields:

       a.   He
       b.   2H
       c.   D
       d.   Li
       e.   None of the above

                                                      Answer: He

9.   Tritium has a half-life of 12.26 y. It decreases to $\frac{1}{4}$ of its original amount in how many years?

       a.   4.1
       b.   6.1
       c.   12.3
       d.   24.5
       e.   None of the above

                                                      Answer: 24.5

10. $^{238}_{92}U$ decays to $^{226}_{88}Ra$ by the emission of alpha and beta particles. The number of beta particles emitted during the decay is:

       a.   1
       b.   2
       c.   3
       d.   4
       e.   None of the above

                                                      Answer: 2

11. ^{12}C contains $1.3 \times 10^{-10}\%$ of ^{14}C in nature (as a percentage of the number of atoms present). The number of ^{14}C atoms in 1.0 g of fresh carbon is:

a. 6.5×10^{10}
b. 1.3×10^{11}
c. 1.3×10^{12}
d. 6.5×10^{12}
e. None of the above

Answer: 6.5×10^{10}

12. ^{12}C contains $1.3 \times 10^{-10}\%$ of ^{14}C in nature (as a percentage of the number of atoms present). The half-life of ^{14}C is 5730 y, the number of decays per minute in 1.0 g of fresh carbon is:

a. 0.75
b. 2.5
c. 12
d. 15
e. None of the above

Answer: 15

13. A decay rate of 1.8×10^8 per second corresponds to what activity (Curies)?

a. 2×10^{-5} Ci
b. 6×10^{-4} Ci
c. 5×10^{-3} Ci
d. 1×10^{-2} Ci
e. None of the above

Answer: 5×10^{-3} Ci

14. The half-life of a radioactive isotope is 4.8 h. If there are 1.5×10^{23} atoms of this material initially, how many atoms remain after 36 h?

a. 2.8×10^{16} atoms
b. 4.8×10^{18} atoms
c. 2.4×10^{19} atoms
d. 8.3×10^{20} atoms
e. None of the above

Answer: 8.3×10^{20} atoms

15. The isotope of carbon, C^{14} has half-life of 5730yr. If at some time a sample contains 1.00×10^{22} C^{14} nuclei, what is the activity of the sample?

a. 2.44×10^{16} decays/s
b. 4.81×10^{18} decays/s
c. 3.83×10^{11} decays/s
d. 8.32×10^{20} decays/s
e. None of the decays/s

Answer: 3.83×10^{11} atoms

16. A laboratory has a sample having mass $1.49\mu g$ of pure N^{13} isotope which has life-time of 10.0min. How long it will take for the activity to drop to less than 1decay/s?

   a.   7.66h
   b.   24h
   c.   30min
   d.   14h
   e.   None of the above

Answer: 7.66h

17. Thorium $\left(^{232}_{90}\text{Th}\right)$ decays to lead $\left(^{208}_{82}\text{Pb}\right)$ by alpha and beta decay. The total number of alpha and beta decays are:

   a.   6
   b.   8
   c.   9
   d.   10
   e.   None of the above

Answer: 10

31.0 - PROBLEMS

18. The half-life of radium is 1620 y. (a) Calculate the activity in Becquerel of 1.0 g of radium (226.025 g/mole). (b) Radium decays by alpha emission to radon (222.0175 g/mole). If the energy released goes into kinetic energy of the alpha particle, calculate this energy.
Answer: (a) 3.6×10^{10} Bq; (b) 4.56 MeV

19. Radioactivity of an isotope is measured as 9600 Bq. 24 min later it is measured as 720 Bq. (a) Calculate the decay parameter, λ, the reciprocal of the time constant of decay. (b) Calculate the half-life of the isotope.
Answer: (a) 1.8×10^{-3}/s; (b) 385 s

20. Tritium is created by the fissioning of ^{6}Li by a neutron (1.008665 u). (a) Using Table 32.1, calculate the energy released/absorbed in the reaction. (b) If energy of the products is apportioned inversely to mass, calculate the kinetic energy of the tritium nucleus.
Answer: (a) 4.78 MeV; (b) 2.73 MeV

21. A wooden artifact contains 500 g of carbon of which $1.3 \times 10^{-10}\%$ was originally ^{14}C. The artifact has a measured activity of 74.2 Bq. (a) Calculate the activity when the tree was felled. (b) Calculate the number of half-life of ^{14}C that have passed since the tree was felled. (c) Calculate the age of the wooden artifact.
Answer: (a) 125 Bq; (b) 0.75 (c) 4300 y

22. A bone from an archeological dig contains about 250 g of carbon and is supposed to be 12 000 y old. (a) Calculate the activity that you would expect to measure. (b) If you measure 16 Bq, calculate the bone's actual age.
Answer: (a) 14.6 Bq; (b) 11 300 y

23. A free neutron will spontaneously decay in about 15 min (mean lifetime) to a proton and electron. (a) Write the reaction and identify the other particle (balance spins). (b) Calculate the kinetic energy of the election and other particle from this reaction ($n = 1.0086650$ u, $p = 1.0072765$ u, $e = 0.0005486$ u). (c) Calculate the half-life of a free neutron.

24. The radioactive isotope ^{60}Co with a half-life of 5.24 y is often used as a gamma ray source in medicine. (a) Calculate the mass of ^{60}Co (59.934 u) needed to produce 10 kCi of radiation. (1 Ci $= 3.7 \times 10^{10}$ Bq.) (b) Calculate the time for this gamma ray source to decrease by 10%.

Answer: (a) 8.8 g; (b) 9.6 months

25. ^{238}U (238.0508 u) decays by alpha and beta emission to ^{206}Pb (205.9761 u). The half-life of ^{238}U is 4.47×10^9 y. A rock is assayed as containing 36 mg of ^{238}U and 21 mg of ^{206}Pb (no other isotopes of Pb). (a) Calculate the number of ^{238}U atoms in the rock at time of formation. (b) Calculate the age of the rock.

Answer: (a) 1.5×10^{20}; (b) 3.3×10^9 y

26. Neutron stars can be considered spheres of neutrons packed together like marbles. (a) Calculate the number of neutrons in a 1.0 km diameter neutron star. (b) Calculate the mass of the star. (c) Calculate the ratio of the mass of the star to the mass of planet Earth.

Answer: (a) 5.8×10^{53}; (b) 9.7×10^{26} kg (c) 162

27. ^{239}Pu (239.0521 u) is produced as a by-product in nuclear reactors. ^{239}Pu has a half-life of 2.41×10^4 y. (a) As little as 2.0 mg of ^{239}Pu is lethal to humans. Calculate the number of atoms this amount represents. (b) Calculate the radioactivity of this amount of ^{239}Pu in Curies.

Answer: (a) 5.0×10^{18}; (b) 124 μCi

28. ^{147}Sm (146.915 u) comprises 15% of naturally occurring samarium and decays by alpha emission. A 1.25 g sample of samarium has a measured activity of 150 Bq. (a) Calculate the number of ^{147}Sm atoms in the sample. (b) Calculate the half-life of ^{147}Sm.

Answer: (a) 7.68×10^{20}; (b) 1.1×10^{11} y

29. Our Sun operates on a proton-proton cycle producing helium, gamma rays, and neutrinos according to the simplified equation $4H + 2e \rightarrow {}^4He + 2\nu + 4\gamma$. (a) Calculate the energy released in this reaction. (b) If the Sun radiates at the rate of 3.9×10^{26} W, calculate the mass consumption rate of protons. (c) If the Sun dies when 10% of the protons are consumed, calculate the lifetime of the Sun ($m = 1.99 \times 10^{30}$ kg).

Answer: (a) 26.7 MeV; (b) 6.1×10^{11} kg/s (c) 10^{10} y

30. A typical fission reaction in a nuclear power plant is:
$$^{235}U + n \rightarrow {}^{141}Ba + {}^{92}Kr + bn + Q,$$
where ^{235}U $= 235.04392$ u, ^{141}Ba $= 140.91436$ u, ^{92}Kr $= 91.92627$, $n = 1.00867$ u, and b is some number of neutrons. (a) Calculate the energy produced, Q. (b) Calculate the mass of ^{235}U consumed each year by a 250 MW power plant operating at 50% efficiency of conversion of heat to electricity.

Answer: (a) 173 MeV; (b) 223 kg

31. The D-T reaction is the most promising for producing electricity by nuclear fusion with ^{4}He as the by-product. (a) Calculate the energy produced by this reaction. (b) Tritium is manufactured by neutrons obtained from the D-T reaction that combine with ^{6}Li to form ^{4}He and T. Calculate the energy involved in this reaction.

Answer: (a) 176 MeV; (b) 4.8 MeV

32. In a certain experiment, 0.016Ci of radioactive phosphor isotope P^{32} is injected into a medium containing a culture of bacteria. After one hour, the cells are washed and a detector that is 70% efficient (counts 70% of emitted β-rays) records 720 counts per minute from all the cells. What percentage of the original P^{32} isotope was taken up by the cells?

Answer: 2.9%

33. A neutron is observed to strike O^{16} nucleus and a deuteron is given off. (Deuteron, H^2 is an isotope of Hydrogen!) What is the nucleus that results?

Answer: N^{15} – an isotope of nitrogen!

34. The D-T reaction is the most promising for producing electricity by nuclear fusion with ^{4}He as the by-product, and considering a 250 MW power plant operating at 50% efficiency of conversion of heat to electricity, (a) calculate the mass of deuterium consumed per year. (b) Calculate the mass of lithium consumed per year.

Answer: (a) 1.82 kg; (b) 5.42 kg

CHAPTER 31

31.0 - MULTIPLE CHOICE QUESTIONS

1. The lepton number of an electron is:

   a.   1/2
   b.   −1/2
   c.   +1
   d.   −1
   e.   None of the above

                                        Answer: +1

2. The lepton number of a positron is:

   a.   1/2
   b.   −1/2
   c.   +1
   d.   −1
   e.   None of the above

                                        Answer: −1

3. The proton is a:

   a.   Baryon
   b.   Kaon
   c.   Lepton
   d.   Meson
   e.   None of the above

                                        Answer: Baryon

4. A high energy photon near a nucleus can cause an electron-positron pair production. What is the least energy of the photon?

   a.   0.511 MeV
   b.   1.022 MeV
   c.   1.533 MeV
   d.   2.044 MeV
   e.   None of the above

                                        Answer: 1.022 MeV

5. In elementary particle interactions, which of the following is not conserved:

   a.   Charge
   b.   Energy
   c.   Momentum
   d.   Angular momentum
   e.   None of the above

                                        Answer: None of the above

6. Free neutrons decay to protons, electrons, and antineutrinos by which of the following types of interaction?

   a. Electromagnetic
   b. Weak
   c. Strong
   d. Gravitational
   e. None of the above

   Answer: Weak

7. The pion, π^0, decays by which of the following types of interaction?

   a. Electromagnetic
   b. Weak
   c. Strong
   d. Gravitational
   e. None of the above

   Answer: Electromagnetic

8. The muon, μ^-, decays into an electron and neutrinos. Their total kinetic energy is:

   a. 0.511 MeV
   b. 9.8 MeV
   c. 51 MeV
   d. 105 MeV
   e. None of the above

   Answer: 105 MeV

9. Quarks and antiquarks have the same:

   a. Charge
   b. Spin
   c. Baryon number
   d. Charm
   e. None of the above

   Answer: Spin

10. There are which of the following number of types of quarks?

    a. 2
    b. 4
    c. 6
    d. 8
    e. None of the above

    Answer: 6

11. The quark composition of an antiproton is:

    a. uud

206

b.   udd
c. $\overline{u}u\overline{d}$
d. $\overline{u}d\overline{d}$
e.   None of the above

Answer: $\overline{u}u\overline{d}$

12.   A particle has a charge of +e, spin of zero, and strangeness zero. It can be made from which of the following quarks and antiquarks?

a.   uud
b. $u\overline{d}$
c. $\overline{u}d$
d. $s\overline{c}$
e.   None of the above

Answer: $u\overline{d}$

13.   A small cyclotron of maximum radius of 0.25m accelerates protons in a 1.7T magnetic field. Calculate the needed frequency of the applied alternating voltage!

a.   260 MHz
b.   254 kHz
c.   314 MHz
d.   628 kHz
e.   None of the above

Answer: 260 MHz.

14.   A small cyclotron of maximum radius of 0.25m accelerates protons in a 1.7T magnetic field. Calculate the kinetic energy of protons when they leave the cyclotron!

a.   8.8 MeV
b.   12.4 MeV
c.   7.2 MeV
d.   1.2 MeV
e.   None of the above

Answer: 8.8 MeV

15.   A fermion particle has zero charge, a baryon number of +1, and a strangeness of -1, charm of zero, bottomness zero, and topness zero. The particle is composed of:

a.   ubs
b. $u\overline{u}s$
c. $u\overline{c}$
d.   uds
e.   None of the above

Answer: uds

16.   The reaction, $p + \pi^+ \rightarrow \Lambda^0 + K^+$, violates which conservation law?

a.   Charge
b.   Spin

c.   Lepton number
d.   Baryon number
e.   None of the above

Answer: Charge

17.   The reaction, $e + \nu \rightarrow \pi^- + \pi^0$, violates which conservation law?

a.   Charge
b.   Spin
c.   Lepton number
d.   Baryon number
e.   None of the above

Answer: Lepton number

31.0 - PROBLEMS

18.   Pions, π^+, at rest have a mean life of 26 ns and spontaneously decay into a muon, μ^+, and muon neutrino. (a) Calculate the kinetic energy of the μ^+ and ν. (b) If the kinetic energy of the muon is 4.10 MeV, calculate the momentum of the ν. (c) Calculate the momentum of the μ^+.
Answer: (a) 33.9 MeV; (b) 29.8 MeV/c; (c) 29.8 MeV/c

19.   An antikaon, K^-, bombards protons in a LH bubble chamber producing an antipion, π^-, and baryon, Σ^+. (a) Calculate the values of the seven quantum numbers: spin, charge, baryon number, strangeness, charm, bottomness, and topness of the $K^- + p$ reaction. (b) Calculate these numbers for the $\pi^- + \Sigma^+$ product. (c) Calculate the energy released in the reaction.
Answer: (a) $\frac{1}{2}, 0, 1, -1, 0, 0, 0$;   (b) $\frac{1}{2}, 0, 1, -1, 0, 0, 0$;   (c) 103 MeV

20.   In a proton-antiproton annihilation in which the protons are essentially at rest, two photons are produced. (a) Why are two photons required? (b) Calculate the energy of each photon. (c) Calculate the magnitude of momentum of each photon.
Answer: (a) To conserve E and p; (b) 938.3 MeV; (c) 5.0×10^{-19} kg $\cdot$ m/s

21.   In a proton-antiproton production by a gamma ray, (a) why are both the proton and antiproton required in the reaction? (b) Calculate the minimum energy of the gamma ray photon. (c) Calculate the magnitude of momentum of the proton.
Answer: (a) To conserve spins, p and q; (b) 1.88 GeV; (c) 5.0×10^{-19} kg $\cdot$ m/s

22.   (a) Calculate the approximate range of the strong force if a π^+ pion is the mediating particle. (b) Calculate the approximate range of the strong force if a K^+ kaon is the mediating particle.
Answer: (a) 0.71 fm; (b) 0.20 fm

23.   A hadron can sometimes emit a virtual proton-antiproton pair. (a) From the Uncertainty Principle, calculate the approximate time that this pair can exist. (b) Calculate the distance the pair can travel at 0.95 c.
Answer: (a) 3.5×10^{-25} s; (b) 0.10 fm

24.   A hadron can sometimes emit a virtual proton-antiproton pair. (a) calculate the gravitational attraction between the proton and antiproton. (b) Calculate the electrostatic attraction between the proton and antiproton. (c) Calculate the ratio of the gravitational and electrostatic attractions.
Answer: (a) 1.87×10^{-32} N; (b) 2.30×10^4 N; (c) 8.1×10^{-37}

25. An early cyclotron at UC Berkeley could accelerate a deuteron to 5.0 MeV in a 75 cm diameter path. (a) Calculate the final speed of the deuteron. (b) Calculate the final magnetic flux required for the cyclotron.

Answer: (a) 2.2×10^7 m/s; (b) 1.22 T

26. A 20 GeV electron from the SLAC accelerator races a photon signal down a 100 m evacuated tube. (a) Calculate by what amount the speed of the electron is less than the speed of the photon signal. (b) Calculate by what distance the electron lags behind the photon signal at the end of the tube.

Answer: (a) 0.098 m/s; (b) 32.6 nm

27. The Xi minus baryon has the same charge and spin as the electron but has a strangeness of -2. It is known to be a combination of three quarks. (a) What are they? (b) What is the resulting baryon number?

Answer: (a) dss; (b) $+1$

28. Weak interactions have the boson intermediaries $W^{\pm}$ (82 GeV) and Z (92 GeV). (a) Calculate the approximate range of the $W^{\pm}$ interaction. (b) Calculate the approximate range of the Z interaction.

Answer: (a) 0.0012 fm; (b) 0.0011 fm

29. K^- hadrons bombarding a LH bubble chamber initially produces the reaction $K^- + p \rightarrow \Omega^- + K^+ + K^0$. (a) Calculate the spin, charge, baryon number, and strangeness on the left of this reaction. (b) Calculate the spin, charge, baryon number, and strangeness of the Ω^- particle.

Answer: (a) $\frac{1}{2}$, 0, 1, -1; (b) $\frac{1}{2}$, -1, 1, -3

30. Which of the following decay schemes are possible for the muon decay:
    (i) $\mu^- \rightarrow e^- + \overline{\nu}_e$
    (ii) $\mu^- \rightarrow e^- + \overline{\nu}_e + \nu_{\mu}$
    (iii) $\mu^- \rightarrow e^- + \nu_e$

Answer: Reaction (ii) can go. The other two do not have all "lepton" numbers conserved!

31. What are the wavelengths of the two photons produced when a proton-antiproton pair at rest annihilate?

Answer: 1.32×10^{-15}m.

32. Using the relativistic energy triangle and that the total energy of a particle is the sum of kinetic and rest energies, (a) show that $pc = [(KE)^2 + 2(KE)mc^2]^{1/2}$. (b) For the pion decay, $\pi^- \rightarrow \mu^- + \overline{\nu}$, with 33.9 MeV of energy released and using the equation in (a) with the conservation of momentum (i.e., $p_{\mu} = p_{\nu}$), calculate the kinetic energy of the muon.

Answer: (b) 4.1 MeV